Geometry Activities

FOR MIDDLE SCHOOL STUDENTS

with

KAREN WINDHAM WYATT

ANN LAWRENCE

GINA M. FOLETTA

Key Curriculum Press
Innovators in Mathematics Education

Editors	Dan Bennett, John Bergez, Daniel Ditty
Editorial Assistant	Lori Dixon
Advisor	William Finzer
Reviewers	Ellen M. Cooch, David Rock, Mary Ann Rota, Susan Smolin, Anne C. Thompson
Editorial Production Manager	Debbie Cogan
Production Editors	Jennifer Strada, Kristin Ferraioli
Copyeditor	Erin Milnes
Production Director	Diana Jean Parks
Production Coordinator	Mike Hurtik
Interior Design	Kirk Mills
Art	Laura Murray Productions
Art and Design Coordinator	Kavitha Becker
Cover Photo	Rex Butcher/Bruce Coleman Inc.
Prepress and Printer	Data Reproductions
Executive Editor	Casey FitzSimons
Publisher	Steven Rasmussen

Photo credit: Photo on page ix supplied by the authors. Pictured (left to right) are Ann Lawrence, Charlie Adams, Brittany Beth, Karen Windham Wyatt, and David Sloan.

®The Geometer's Sketchpad, ®Dynamic Geometry, and ®Key Curriculum Press are registered trademarks of Key Curriculum Press. ™Sketchpad is a trademark of Key Curriculum Press. All other registered trademarks and trademarks in this book are the property of their respective owners.

***Geometry Activities for Middle School Students with The Geometer's Sketchpad* CD-ROM**

Key Curriculum Press guarantees that the *Geometry Activities for Middle School Students with The Geometer's Sketchpad* CD-ROM that accompanies this book is free of defects in materials and workmanship. A defective disk will be replaced free of charge if returned within 90 days of the purchase date. After 90 days, there is a $10.00 replacement fee.

Key Curriculum Press
1150 65th Street
Emeryville, CA 94608
510-595-7000
editorial@keypress.com
http://www.keypress.com

Printed in the United States of America   10 9 8 7 6 5   11 10 09 08   ISBN 978-1-55953-647-9

About the Authors

During the last twenty-five years, Karen Windham Wyatt has taught middle school mathematics, high school mathematics, and computer programming, and she has served as Secondary Mathematics Facilitator for Mountain Brook City Schools in Birmingham, Alabama. With Ann Lawrence, she has co-authored and received several grants along with local, state, and national recognition. She served as co-editor of the Software Review section for *Mathematics Teaching in the Middle School,* a journal of the National Council of Teachers of Mathematics (NCTM). She has presented various Sketchpad™ workshops and institutes at both the middle school and high school levels. She is currently serving as the mathematics department coordinator of Mountain Brook Junior High School in Birmingham, Alabama, where she also teaches geometry and advanced geometry. You can contact her at wyattk@mtnbrook.k12.al.us.

Ann Lawrence has taught middle school mathematics for over twenty years. During those years, she has pursued a range of related endeavors, from co-coaching a national champion MATHCOUNTS team to serving as cartoon editor and co-editor of the Software Review section for the NCTM journal, *Mathematics Teaching in the Middle School*. She has served as coordinator of the mathematics department at Mountain Brook Junior High School in Birmingham, Alabama; a T3 instructor for graphing calculators and professional development initiatives; a member of the K–8 Leadership Institute for Discrete Mathematics; and project director for PBS MathLine's Algebraic Thinking Mathematics Project. She has conducted workshops and consulted for schools and school districts nationwide. Currently, Ann Lawrence teaches mathematics and technology classes at Capitol Hill Day School in Washington, D.C. Her publications include a book of mathematical investigations for Texas Instruments and a book of lessons to foster the development of algebraic thinking for Math Solutions Publications. You can contact her at AnnLTeach@aol.com.

Gina M. Foletta, Ph.D., has taught high school mathematics in California and Iowa. She is currently assistant professor of mathematics at Northern Kentucky University. Dr. Foletta has worked extensively with pre-service and in-service teachers, especially in the areas of geometry and technology. She is currently co-directing the Kentucky Partnership for Reform Initiatives in Science and Mathematics (PRISM) Secondary Mathematics Initiative in northern Kentucky. Underlying all of her work is an interest in appropriate uses of technology in the learning and teaching of mathematics. You can contact her at foletta@nku.edu.

Contents

Unit 4: Quadrilaterals

Unit 5: Symmetry

Unit 6: Transformations

Unit 7: Constructions

A Note to Teachers

Interactive computer software provides abundant opportunities to enhance the way we teach mathematics. Beyond the obvious advantage of electronic practice, software programs increase the options for presentation of new material and independent student investigations. Perhaps the possibilities have expanded most for the teaching of geometry. Using The Geometer's Sketchpad®, for example, students can explore concepts much more easily than in the past. The ability to create and manipulate figures on the computer enables students to quickly visualize and pro-

duce many examples, examine properties of the figures, look for patterns, and make conjectures. This capability is especially exciting because these steps are essential for most students to truly understand even the basic concepts of geometry.

As teachers of middle school students, we deal with students at the age when they are beginning to think abstractly; also, the mathematics curriculum for this age group includes the introduction of many of the concepts that lay the foundation for the formal study of geometry. Thus, it is during these years that students need exactly the kinds of experiences that The Geometer's Sketchpad makes possible.

We believe that students should discover for themselves as many of the ideas and relationships of geometry as possible. Of course, when first encountering this approach students need more guidance down the path to discovery than they do later. Nevertheless, we have found that carefully constructed activities enable our middle school students to experience the joy of discovering mathematics, the confidence that comes with success, and the framework for a pattern of independent learning.

With these experiences in mind, we have developed the units in this book for teachers to use with The Geometer's Sketchpad in middle school mathematics classes. The materials are designed to be flexible. They may be used as the basis for an independent geometry unit for a middle school, as a set of activities for reinforcement or enrichment for a text-based unit, or as individual activities to be woven into the mathematics curriculum on appropriate occasions.

Content and Organization

Units 2 through 6 each focus on a cluster of geometric concepts that are usually introduced during the middle school years. They are grouped as follows:

Unit 2: Points, Lines, and Angles
Unit 3: Triangles
Unit 4: Quadrilaterals
Unit 5: Symmetry
Unit 6: Transformations

For each of these units, the material is self-contained. Of course, there are activities in each unit that integrate concepts from others, but the primary emphasis is indicated by the unit title. None of the units rely on students having done any other unit, although the Teacher Notes sometimes refer to related activities that might be helpful to do first.

Unit 1 contains tours for getting acquainted with The Geometer's Sketchpad and some of its animation capabilities. Unit 7 contains step-by-step instructions for a variety of constructions that use Sketchpad™ and are suitable for middle school students.

Units 2 through 6 include these components.

1. **Teacher Notes.** The Teacher Notes in each unit include an anecdotal commentary with hints or comments about each activity and project, a list of mathematical concepts, a list of prerequisite Sketchpad skills, definitions of essential vocabulary, and detailed instructions for carrying out Teacher Demonstrations. Also included are writing prompts for student assignments, examples of student work, and answers for both the guided discovery activities and Wrap-Up assignment.

   Sketches for Teacher Demonstrations are included in a folder on the CD-ROM that accompanies this book. You may often find the demonstrations helpful in orienting students before they begin some of the independent activities. The demonstrations help you consider prerequisites, present appropriate mathematical terms, and introduce or review Sketchpad skills needed in the activities.

2. **Activities and Projects.** The activities in each unit provide a framework for students' explorations. Often there are one or two activities requiring very little technical expertise that you will feel comfortable giving your students with little or no guidance beforehand. Other activities maximize guided discovery by students. Some of these are more open-ended than others, and their difficulty levels vary. You should feel free to choose those activities that are most appropriate for the ability and skill levels of your students. In some instances, even though the activities are designed for use with a class of students working alone or in pairs, using the activity as a teacher demonstration will be appropriate. Sketches for these activities are included on the accompanying CD-ROM, and the text provides blackline masters for student work.

   Each unit also contains projects, which are designed to help students explore the unit topic further in small groups or independently. Usually the projects require students to create their own sketches. Each project specifies an objective to accomplish or an area to explore, but specific instructions are not given.

3. **Wrap-Up.** The unit Wrap-Up is a blackline master you can use for individual, in-class reinforcement, as a homework assignment, or as an assessment instrument. The Wrap-Up does not require the use of Sketchpad.

4. **Quick Reference Guide.** These step-by-step instruction sheets enumerate Sketchpad maneuvers needed to carry out the activities in each unit. We have found it helpful to copy a classroom set of each of these reference guides and laminate them. We leave the laminated copies in the computer lab so that students can use them not only when working with their classmates but also when they go to the lab for independent explorations with Sketchpad.

Hints and Suggestions

Especially if you're new to Sketchpad, we suggest working through the Tours, Quick Reference Guides, and Teacher Demonstrations in your preparation for working with students. Becoming familiar with these aids can greatly facilitate your own learning of the software and increase your comfort level with these materials in the classroom or computer lab.

But even if you're using Sketchpad for the first time, don't let your inexperience keep you from placing the software into the hands of your students! One of the best aspects of our first year in the middle school classroom with Sketchpad was learning along with our students. Students and teachers learned and taught one another not only the software but also mathematics. Nothing in the classroom can compare to the excitement generated when students and teacher experience the joy of learning mathematics together.

If you are an adventurous teacher, you may choose to alter or omit the Teacher Demonstrations altogether. Another choice is to let students explore for themselves with the Demo sketches. In our first year we certainly had no notes or predesigned sketches, yet the year was exciting as well as productive.

Regardless of the degree of structure you are comfortable with, be sure to allow time for students to simply explore with the software. Before or after initial activities students love to try the tools and experiment on their own. This free exploration motivates students to want to learn more about the capabilities of Sketchpad, thus helping to provide a rich learning atmosphere.

Finally, we encourage you to allow your students to work in pairs or in small groups for some if not most of the activities. The units in this book, as well as Sketchpad itself, are ideal instruments for cooperative learning. When we teach this way, our students exhibit both increased mathematical understanding and greater Sketchpad proficiency.

Some Comments on Sketchpad Sketches and Techniques

In constructing the sketches that accompany the demonstrations and activities, we have sometimes introduced constraints for pedagogical reasons. We don't want students hampered by their lack of mathematical understanding or Sketchpad proficiency. For example, when the goal is for students to discover the properties of the various types of quadrilaterals, they obviously don't have enough knowledge to construct a rectangle that has the mathematical properties of a rectangle, or they wouldn't need to do the activity! By dragging a rectangle that is constructed to remain a rectangle, they can test to see whether it can be dragged into a square with the confidence that their results are mathematically sound.

Also, some of the sketches have orientation restrictions so that students can avoid distractions and focus on the target concept. In either case, as your students become more experienced with Sketchpad, you may want them to devise more of their own constructions. At some point, you may want to redesign some of our sketches to take fuller advantage of the dynamic features of the software.

There are many quick keys and other shortcuts built into Sketchpad, and these can be terrific time-saving measures. Hints on shortcuts are provided in many of the Quick Reference Guides. However, in our experience, with middle school students it is better to postpone the introduction of most shortcuts, including quick keys, until the students are somewhat familiar with the software.

The primary benefits of waiting are threefold. First, middle school students who are new to Sketchpad often need some experience before they can carry out shortcuts successfully. What seems to be a simple maneuver at a later time can be quite difficult in the beginning. For example, to construct a segment between two points, a Sketchpad user can use the Segment tool ⟋, click on one point, and drag and release on the other point instead of selecting the two points, going to the Construct menu, and choosing Segment. However, when many middle schoolers try to perform this shortcut, they fail to drag the segment near enough to the second endpoint to activate the "snap to" feature. As a result, their figure falls apart eventually, and they are both disappointed and frustrated. Of course, with some experience using Sketchpad, these obstacles disappear.

Second, the speed of the shortcuts, especially during teacher demonstrations, may not provide students with enough time to process the steps that the shortcut replaces. For example, use of the quick key for constructing the midpoint of a segment may be misconstrued as constructing an arbitrary point on the segment. We have found it works far better for students to discover this shortcut on their own or to show them the shortcut later. Once they clearly understand what constructing a midpoint means mathematically, they realize what steps the shortcut replaces.

Third, the visual reinforcement of seeing the labels in the menus for the Sketchpad maneuver strengthens the students' grasp of the mathematical processes they are performing. For example, when designating a segment as a mirror, the user selects the segment, goes to the Transform menu, and chooses Mark Mirror. Going through this use of the menu seems to remind students why the segment is being selected and to help them connect the use of a mirror to the whole concept of transformations.

Sketches on the CD-ROM

As noted above, the CD-ROM that accompanies this book contains Sketchpad sketches for the activities and Teacher Demonstrations. The CD will work on computers running Microsoft Windows® and on computers running the Macintosh® operating system. The CD does not contain The Geometer's Sketchpad program itself. Sketchpad is available separately from Key Curriculum Press.

The sketches are organized in folders by chapter, with separate folders for activity sketches and demo sketches. The Symmetry Demos folder also includes examples of student work on the symmetry project. Be sure to look these over—they're lots of fun.

Origins of This Book

This book originated in the experiences of two of the authors, Karen Windham Wyatt and Ann Lawrence. Our junior high school math department was working to implement the 1989 NCTM Curriculum and Evaluation Standards. We were making progress, but much more slowly than we wished. We took a proposal to our principal and superintendent asking for release time for Karen Windham Wyatt to lead a push to integrate technology into the mathematics curriculum of all our courses. Once we received the go-ahead, all the teachers in our department helped collect ideas for calculator activities, computer topics, and software.

One of our teachers saw a demonstration of The Geometer's Sketchpad at a regional NCTM meeting in the spring of 1993. At the national convention in Seattle that same spring, Karen Windham Wyatt attended the first user group meeting for Sketchpad, and we were sold on the software! We wrote grant proposals and were granted a site license for Sketchpad. Karen Windham Wyatt attended the first five-day Sketchpad Institute in the summer of 1993. The school administration granted her the partial release time we had requested and our year began. We used Sketchpad at all three grade levels with great success. Karen Windham Wyatt kept a journal during that year, so when Key requested feedback from the participants of the Sketchpad Institute, she sent them entries from the journal and copies of the instructions and activities that involved Sketchpad. Key was excited about the ways we were applying Sketchpad in the middle school classroom. They called to ask us whether we were interested in writing a book of middle school activities for Sketchpad. We were and we did!

We held a Sketchpad camp the first summer to refine some of the activities we had tried with our students the previous year and to try out new ideas. During the next two school years we continued the process of developing and refining activities as ideas occurred to us, our fellow teachers, and our students. Gina Foletta joined us for the final major round of revisions, and the materials presented in this book were completed.

Without the help, support, and patience of the other teachers in our department, this book would never have been completed. Likewise, our students gave us inspiration to create and complete the task. Our original team from Key—Bill Finzer, Dan Bennett, Steve Rasmussen, John Bergez, and Jason Luz—were our technical advisors and provided much encouragement. Kirk Mills supplied the interior and cover designs. We would also like to thank Kavitha Becker, Dan Ditty, Lori Dixon, Mike Hurtik, Daniel Scher, and Jennifer Strada for their contributions to this revised edition. We especially want to thank our daughters, Emily and Lori, who put up with ridiculous hours, endured computers even on vacations, and provided solicited and unsolicited editing advice. We are grateful to you all.

When all is said and done, this book is written for children, for that is where our dedication lies.

Karen Windham Wyatt
Ann Lawrence
Gina M. Foletta

Unit 1
TOURS

Commentary

The purpose of the Tours unit is to provide step-by-step instructions so that students will feel comfortable using Sketchpad. **Getting to Know Sketchpad—Tours 1** and **2** will give middle school students the hands-on experience they need as a foundation for building proficiency and confidence in using the software. We highly recommend having students work through these tours before they do other activities in this book.

Animation—Tours 1, 2, 3, and **4** not only provide exposure to Sketchpad animation skills used in later activities, but also act as a springboard for independent student exploration. We have found the animation capabilities of Sketchpad exciting and extremely motivating for every group of middle school students (and teachers!) with whom we have worked. Unlike the two introductory tours, the animation tours can be delayed until you feel they are appropriate. One excellent place to incorporate animation is in the project **Make Me Symmetric** in the Symmetry unit. Whenever you choose to use these tours, you may want to show your students some of our students' animated sketches (found in the **Symmetry** folder). Seeing other students' work has always sparked imaginations!

Getting to Know Sketchpad—Tour 1

Welcome to The Geometer's Sketchpad®, an exciting and useful tool for students of all ages. With Sketchpad™, you can explore geometry in ways you never would be able to otherwise. In **Getting to Know Sketchpad—Tour I,** you will learn some Sketchpad skills that you will use in doing activities and projects. Feel free to explore on your own with the tools as you proceed through the tour.

1. Open a new sketch by choosing **New Sketch** from the File menu. You will use this tour to explore some features of Sketchpad.

2. On the left side of your sketch, you'll see Sketchpad's toolbox, shown below. You will use most of these tools during this tour.

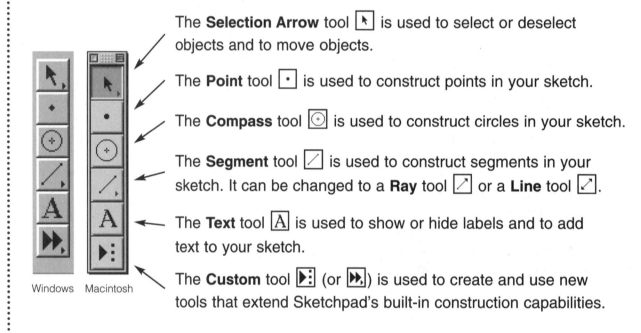

The **Selection Arrow** tool is used to select or deselect objects and to move objects.

The **Point** tool is used to construct points in your sketch.

The **Compass** tool is used to construct circles in your sketch.

The **Segment** tool is used to construct segments in your sketch. It can be changed to a **Ray** tool or a **Line** tool.

The **Text** tool is used to show or hide labels and to add text to your sketch.

The **Custom** tool (or) is used to create and use new tools that extend Sketchpad's built-in construction capabilities.

Windows   Macintosh

The list of words across the top of your screen (see below) is known as the Menu Bar. You will use the various menus to choose commands.

| File | Edit | Display | Construct | Transform | Measure | Graph | Help |

3. Click on the **Point** tool and move onto your sketch. Click in a couple of places to construct points.

4. Click on the **Segment** tool and move onto your sketch. Click and drag to draw a segment.

5. Now construct an angle using the **Segment** tool ⟋. First, draw a segment. Then, starting from one of the segment's endpoints, draw another segment to create an angle. Your screen should look similar to the figure at right.

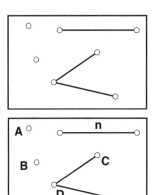

6. Click on the **Text** tool Ⓐ. To show a point's label, position the **Text** tool over the point and click. The hand will turn black. Show some of the point labels. Then click on the segment itself (not the endpoints) to show its label. Your screen should now look similar to the figure at right. Your labels may not be the same as the ones in this example.

7. To move the objects or to change their size, click on the **Selection Arrow** tool ▸. Using this tool, drag one of the endpoints of your segment to make the segment longer or shorter.

8. Drag one of the endpoints of a side of your angle to change the size of the angle.

9. To move the segment, click on the segment itself. The segment should look similar to this when it is selected: ⊶⟞⟝⊶ . While it is selected, drag it. It should move around on your screen without changing its length.

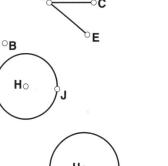

10. Click on the **Compass** tool ⊙. Drag in your sketch to construct a circle. Notice that the center and a point on the circle are always given.

11. Click on the **Selection Arrow** tool ▸ and drag the point on the circle to change the circle's size. Also try dragging the center point to change the size of the circle.

larger   smaller

12. Drag the circle to change its location without changing its size (drag the circle, not the point on the circle).

13. Click on the segment to select it again. Go to the Measure menu and choose **Length.** The measure for your segment should appear on your screen.

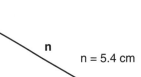

14. Drag one of the endpoints of your segment. The measure on your screen should change as you drag.

$n = 3.0$ cm

15. Choose the **Selection Arrow** tool [arrow], then click in any blank space on your screen. This click deselects everything. You need everything deselected so that you can select the necessary points to measure your angle.

16. Click on the three points that define the angle, with the vertex point your middle selection. When you have them all selected, they should look similar to the diagram at right.

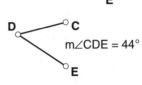

17. While the points are selected, go to the Measure menu and choose **Angle.** You should see the measure of your angle appear on your screen.

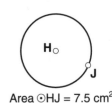

m∠CDE = 44°

18. Click in any blank space on your screen to deselect all objects. Drag the endpoint of one of the angle's sides and observe the changing angle measure. Drag the angle into an acute angle, a right angle, and then an obtuse angle.

19. Click in any blank space to deselect objects. Click on the circle (not the point on the circle) to select it, then go to the Measure menu and choose **Circumference, Area,** or **Radius.** The measure you choose should appear on your screen.

H○

J

Area ⊙HJ = 7.5 cm²

Note: If any measure appears on your screen in an undesirable location, you may drag it to a different position on the screen.

20. Choose the **Text** tool [A] and double-click in a blank area at the top of your sketch to create a text box.

21. Type your name(s) in this box.

Jonathan and Sammy

Summary

In this tour, you have learned to

- Use the **Selection Arrow** tool [arrow] to select and move objects
- Use the **Selection Arrow** tool [arrow] to deselect objects
- Use the **Point** tool [•] to construct points in your sketch
- Use the **Compass** tool [⊙] to construct circles in your sketch
- Use the **Segment** tool [/] to construct segments in your sketch
- Use the **Text** tool [A] to show labels and to add text to your sketch
- Change the size of objects in your sketch
- Measure objects in your sketch

Getting to Know Sketchpad—Tour 2

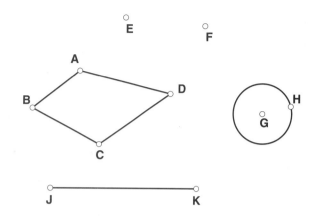

1. Open the sketch **Tour2.gsp.** You will use this sketch to explore some other features of Sketchpad.

Use the **Selection Arrow** tool [↖] while working on steps 2–5.

2. To construct a segment between two given points, click on points **E** and **F** in your sketch. Go to the Construct menu and choose **Segment** to construct $\overline{EF}$, the segment between **E** and **F**.

3. Click in any blank space in your sketch to deselect objects.

4. To construct a point on a circle, click on the circle in your sketch (not on point **H**). The circle should look like the figure at right when selected. Go to the Construct menu and choose **Point On Circle.** A new point should appear on your circle. Drag the new point. Notice that it moves freely around the circle, but you cannot drag it off the circle. Drag point **H**. Because point **H** is one of the control points of the circle, dragging it will change the size of the circle.

5. Click on $\overline{JK}$, go to the Construct menu, and choose **Point On Segment.** Try dragging the new point that appears on $\overline{JK}$. Notice that it will slide along $\overline{JK}$ but you cannot move it off the segment.

Use the **Text** tool [A] while working on steps 6 and 7.

6. To move a label to a new position, position the **Text** tool [A] over the label, not on the object itself. An "A" will appear on the hand. Click on the letter **B** in your sketch. It should look like the figure on the right when you hold down the mouse button. Drag the **B** around. Notice that you can move the label, but you cannot move it very far from the object it names. Try dragging other labels in your sketch.

7. To rename a label, double-click on the label you wish to change. Double-click on the letter **G**. You should see the dialog box shown at right.

Type **P** to replace the letter **G**. Click OK. The new name for the center of your circle should appear.

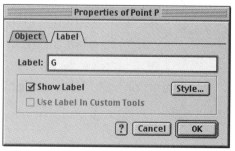

Properties Dialog Box (Macintosh)

Use the **Selection Arrow** tool 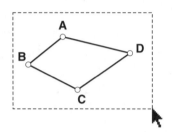 while working on steps 8–21.

8. You've already seen how you can select an object by clicking on it. Now you will learn another way to select one or more objects. Position the arrow in a blank area above and to the left of the quadrilateral. Drag down and to the right so that a dashed box surrounds the quadrilateral.

9. Release the mouse button. All objects inside the box should be selected. This method of selecting objects is known as "using a selection marquee."

10. While it is still selected, drag any vertex or side of the quadrilateral. Notice that when all its parts are selected, you can move it without changing its shape.

11. Use the **Selection Arrow** tool ⬚ to click in any blank space to deselect all objects.

12. To construct a polygon interior, click on the vertex points **A**, **B**, **C**, and **D** in clockwise or counter-clockwise order. Go to the Construct menu and choose **Quadrilateral Interior.** While it is selected, you may change the shade or color of the interior by going to the Display menu and choosing **Color.**

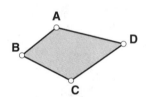

13. To construct the circle interior, click on the circle (not on one of the points on the circle). Go to the Construct menu and choose **Circle Interior.** You may use the Display menu to change the shade of the circle interior if you like.

14. To construct the midpoint of a line segment, click on $\overline{EF}$. Go to the Construct menu and choose **Midpoint.** Drag point **F** and observe that the midpoint remains a midpoint regardless of the change in length of the segment.

15. To hide $\overline{JK}$, click on $\overline{JK}$, go to the Display menu, and choose **Hide Segment.** The points **J** and **K** should remain even though the segment is hidden.

16. To hide several objects at once, you may use a selection marquee. Use the **Selection Arrow** tool ⬚ to drag a box around quadrilateral **ABCD** and circle **P**. Go to the Display menu and choose **Hide Objects.**

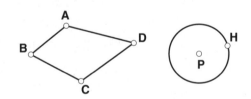

Geometry Activities for Middle School Students with The Geometer's Sketchpad
©2004 Key Curriculum Press

17. To construct a line perpendicular to segment **EF** through point **F**, click on point **F** and then on segment **EF**. Go to the Construct menu and choose **Perpendicular Line.** Drag point **E**. The line remains perpendicular.

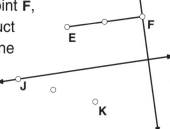

18. Use the **Selection Arrow** tool 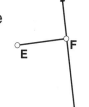 to click in any blank space to deselect all objects.

19. To construct a line parallel to $\overline{EF}$ through point **J**, click on point **J** and on $\overline{EF}$. Go to the Construct menu and choose **Parallel Line.** Drag point **E**. The lines remain parallel.

20. To construct a ray in your sketch, press and hold down the mouse button on the **Segment** tool ⟋. Drag to the right and choose the **Ray** tool ⟋. Click and drag to draw a ray in your sketch.

21. To construct a line in your sketch, press and hold down the mouse button on the **Ray** tool ⟋. Drag to the right and choose the **Line** tool ⟋. Drag to draw a line in your sketch.

22. Click on the **Selection Arrow** tool ⬑. Drag one of the control points that appears on your ray or line. You should be able to change the direction of the line or ray when you drag.

23. Click on the **Text** tool A and double-click in a blank space at the top of your sketch to make a text box.

24. Type your name(s) inside the box.

Sally and Felicity Ann

Summary

In this tour, you have learned to

- Construct a segment between two points using the Construct menu
- Construct a point on an object
- Construct the midpoint of a segment
- Construct rays and lines
- Construct perpendicular and parallel lines
- Construct circle and polygon interiors
- Move labels and change the name of a label
- Select objects by using a selection marquee
- Hide objects

An exciting feature of Sketchpad is animation. Animation in Sketchpad is the ability to give movement to constructed objects. You will discover many ways that animation will add a new dimension to your sketches as you explore. In this tour, you'll begin to learn how to create animations in Sketchpad.

1. Open the sketch **Animation.gsp.** Be sure the page "Tour 1" is showing.

2. Use the **Selection Arrow** tool ▶ to drag a marquee around all the objects in the sketch to select them.

3. Go to the Edit menu and choose **Action Buttons.** Then from the submenu choose **Animation.**

4. When the Animate dialog box appears, click OK.

5. When the Animation button appears, click once on the button to start your animation.

6. The objects in your sketch should begin to move around randomly in the sketch.

7. Click again on the Animation button to stop the animation.

8. Go to the Edit menu and choose **Edit Undo** until the objects return to their original positions.

9. Click in a blank space to deselect objects.

Now you will animate the two points on the circle to see the different ways they behave during animation.

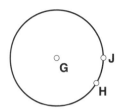

10. Notice that there are two points on the circle. Drag point **H** and observe that it is one of the control points of the circle. It changes the size of the circle.

11. Click on point **H**, go to the Edit menu, and choose **Action Buttons.** Then from the submenu, choose **Animation.** Click OK.

12. Click once on the *Animate Point* button to start the animation. Point **H** should begin to move randomly in the sketch, changing the size of the circle as it moves because it is one on the control points used to construct the circle.

13. Click again on the Animation button to stop the animation. Go to the Edit menu and choose **Edit Undo** to return objects to their original position. Click in a blank space to deselect objects.

14. Drag point **J**. It was constructed as a point on an object. It moves freely around the circle but does not change the size of the circle.

15. With point **J** selected, go to the Edit menu and choose **Action Buttons.** Then from the submenu, choose **Animation.** A dialog box like the one at right appears.

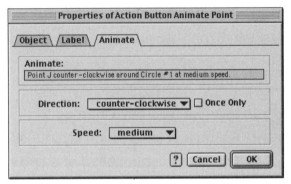

Properties Dialog Box (Macintosh)

16. Change the speed and direction of the animation if you wish, using the drop-down lists on the Animate tab.

17. Click on the Label tab and change the name of the Animation button if you wish. Then click OK.

18. Click on the new Animation button to start the animation. Notice that this action button causes the point to travel around the circle but does not change the size or position of the circle. This point was constructed as a point on the circle and travels freely around the path of the circle.

19. Click on your Animation button again to stop the animation.

Now you will change the speed of your animation from the Display menu.

20. Select point **J** and click on your Animation button. Go to the Display menu and choose either **Increase Speed** or **Decrease Speed** to change the speed of your animated objects.

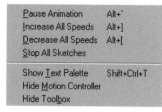

Display Menu (Windows)

21. You can also use the Motion Controller to vary speed or direction of the animation. To open the Motion Controller, go to the Display menu and choose **Show Motion Controller.**

22. Click on each Animation button once to see all your animations at the same time.

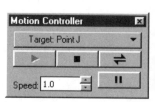

Motion Controller Dialog Box (Windows)

23. Click each button once to stop your animation.

24. Go to the Edit menu and choose **Undo Animate Points.**

25. Click on the **Text** tool A and double-click at the top of your screen to create a text box.

26. Type your name(s) inside the box.

Sherry and Savannah

Summary

In this tour, you have learned to

- Animate objects randomly in a sketch
- Animate a control point of a circle
- Animate a free point on a circle
- Change the speed of animated objects
- Change the name of an Animation button

Animation—Tour 2

In Animation Tours 2, 3, and 4, you will learn techniques for controlling the paths of objects during animation in Sketchpad.

1. Go to the "Jack" page of the sketch **Animation.gsp.** One side of Jack's face was constructed, and then that half was reflected across a vertical mirror to complete his face. Therefore, when you animate one side of the face, the animation will occur on both sides.

Follow steps 2–11 to animate Jack's hair.

2. To animate Jack's hair, use the **Segment** tool ⬚ to construct short segments close to Jack's hair. Your sketch should look similar to the drawing at right.

3. Click on the **Selection Arrow** tool ⬚ and click in a blank space to deselect objects.

4. Select a point on the hair and then select the segment (not its endpoints) closest to that point. Go to the Edit menu and choose **Merge Point To Segment.**

5. Click in a blank space to deselect objects. Repeat the process by selecting the next point on Jack's hair and the segment closest to it and then choosing **Merge Point To Segment.**

6. Click in a blank space to deselect objects. Repeat the process until each point on Jack's hair is merged to a segment close to it. Your sketch should look similar to the drawing at right.

7. Select each point that you merged to the segments (not the endpoints of the segments). Go to the Edit menu and choose **Action Buttons.** Choose **Animation** from the submenu.

8. Change the speed and direction of the animation if you wish using the dialog box. You can also click on the Label tab and change the name of the button if you wish. Click OK.

9. An Animation button should appear in your sketch. Click it once to see the animation.

10. Click again on the button to stop the animation. Then click in a blank space to deselect objects.

11. To hide the segments, their endpoints, and the points you merged, click on each object until you have selected them all. Go to the Display menu and choose **Hide Objects.**

Follow steps 12–23 to construct animated pupils in Jack's eyes.

12. Click on the **Segment** tool ⌀.

13. Draw a small segment in your sketch similar to the one shown at right. This will be the control radius for the pupil.

14. Using the **Selection Arrow** tool ⬆, click in a blank space to deselect objects. Then click on the inner circle of one eye (not the center point). Go to the Construct menu and choose **Point On Circle.**

15. Be sure the point that appeared on your small circle is selected and then click on the control radius segment.

16. Go to the Construct menu and choose **Circle By Center+Radius.** Drag an endpoint of your control radius segment to change the size of the pupil so that it fits inside the eye.

17. To animate this pupil inside the eye, use the **Selection Arrow** tool ⬆. Click in a blank space to deselect objects. Click on the center point of the new circle.

18. Go to the Edit menu and choose **Action Buttons.** Choose **Animation** from the submenu. In the dialog box, click on the Label tab and change the name of the button if you like. Click OK.

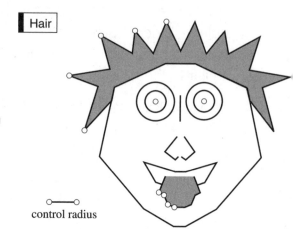

control radius

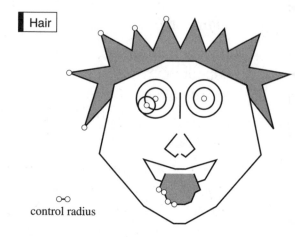

control radius

19. Using the **Selection Arrow** tool [↖], click in a blank space to deselect objects.

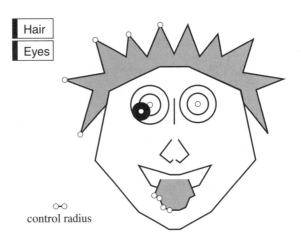

20. To fill in the pupil, click on the pupil circle. Go to the Construct menu and choose **Circle Interior.**

21. Hide the middle circle and the center point of the eyes. To do this, use the **Selection Arrow** tool [↖]. Click in a blank space to deselect objects. Click on the middle-sized circles and the center points of both eyes. Go to the Display menu and choose **Hide Objects.**

22. To reflect the new pupil into the other eye, use the **Selection Arrow** tool [↖]. Click on the vertical segment between the eyes. Go to the Transform menu and choose **Mark Mirror.**

23. Click on the circle and circle interior of the pupil. Go to the Transform menu and choose **Reflect.** Click on your Animation button to see the animation.

Follow steps 24–33 to animate Jack's tongue.

24. Click in a blank space to deselect objects. To move the tongue up and down, use the **Segment** tool [/] to construct a short vertical segment.

25. While the vertical segment is selected, go to the Edit menu and choose **Copy.**

26. Go to the Edit menu and choose **Paste.** Paste three more times so that you have four copies of the vertical segment pasted in your sketch.

27. Using the **Selection Arrow** tool [↖], click in a blank space to deselect objects.

28. Select all the endpoints of your newly copied segments (do not select the segments themselves). Go the Display menu and choose **Hide Points.**

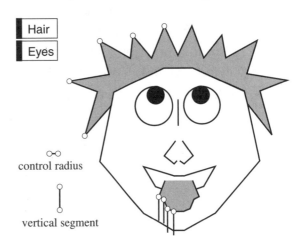

29. Drag each vertical segment directly below one of the four points of Jack's tongue as shown in the figure at right.

30. Using the **Selection Arrow** tool [↖] click in a blank space to deselect objects.

31. Select a point on the tongue and select the segment directly below that point. Go to the Edit menu and choose **Merge Point To Segment.**

32. Click in a blank space to deselect objects. Repeat the process until each point on Jack's tongue is merged to the segment directly below it.

33. Select each point that you merged to the segments. Go to the Edit menu and choose **Action Buttons.** Choose **Animation** from the submenu. In the dialog box click on the Label tab and change the name of the Animation button if you wish but leave the speed settings the same. Click OK.

34. Using the **Selection Arrow** tool, click in a blank space to deselect objects. Click on all the vertical segments to select them. Go to the Display menu and choose **Hide Segments.**

35. Hide any other unwanted segments and points.

36. Click on each of the Animation buttons to watch the animation. What a lovely Jack!

37. Experiment on your own.

38. Using the **Text** tool, double-click in a blank space to create a text box.

39. Type your name(s) inside the box.

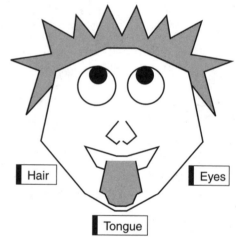

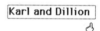

Summary

In this tour, you have learned to

- Animate a point on a polygon (the hair) along a segment to move part of the polygon
- Construct a circle (the pupil of the eye) using a control radius segment and animate the center of the circle around another circle
- Animate a polygon (the tongue) on congruent segments at the same speed so that the polygon animates and its shape is preserved
- Reflect an animated object (the pupil) over a mirror

In this tour, you will learn more techniques of animation in Sketchpad. You will animate a basketball so that it appears to be dribbled and shot through the basket.

1. Go to the "Basket" page of the sketch **Animation.gsp.**

Follow steps 2–14 to construct a ball and have it move through the basket.

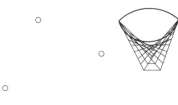

2. Use the **Point** tool ⊡ to construct three points in a blank space to the left of the basket.

3. Using the **Selection Arrow** tool ⊡, click in a blank space to deselect objects. Select the three points in order from left to right. Go to the Construct menu and choose **Arc Through 3 Points.**

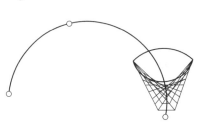

4. Drag one of the endpoints of your arc until you have the arc positioned so that it appears to pass through the basket.

5. Use the **Segment** tool ⊡ to construct a short segment somewhere in the blank area of your sketch.

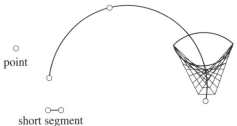

point

6. Use the **Point** tool ⊡ to construct a point somewhere in the blank area of the sketch.

short segment

7. Using the **Selection Arrow** tool ⊡, click in a blank space to deselect objects. Click on both the point and the short segment to select them. (Remember to click on the segment, not its endpoints.)

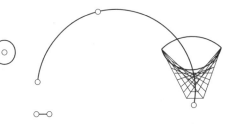

8. Go to the Construct menu and choose **Circle By Center+Radius.** Drag an endpoint of the short segment to change the size of the ball.

9. Using the **Selection Arrow** tool ⊡, click in a blank space to deselect objects. Click on the center point of the ball and then click on the arc to select it. (Do not click on the points on the arc.)

10. Go to the Edit menu and choose **Merge Point To Arc.**

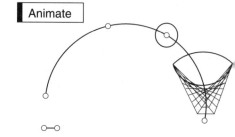

11. While the center point of the ball is selected, go to the Edit menu and choose **Action Buttons.** Choose **Animation** from the submenu. In the dialog box, change the direction to **forward.** Click OK.

12. Click on the new Animation button to see your animation.

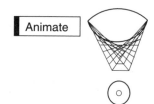

13. Click once on the button to stop the animation. Click in a blank space with the **Selection Arrow** tool to deselect objects. Click on the arc and its three defining points and the short segment and its endpoints.

14. Go to the Display menu and choose **Hide Objects.** Click on the Animation button again. Notice that the ball still moves along the arc even though the arc is hidden.

Follow steps 15–25 to create a bouncing ball in your sketch.

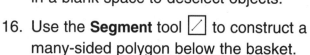

15. Using the **Selection Arrow** tool, click in a blank space to deselect objects.

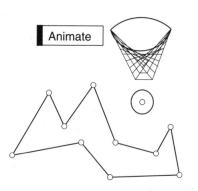

16. Use the **Segment** tool to construct a many-sided polygon below the basket.

17. Using the **Selection Arrow** tool, click in a blank space to deselect objects.

18. Select the vertex points of your polygon in clockwise or counterclockwise order.

19. Go to the Construct menu and choose **Polygon Interior.**

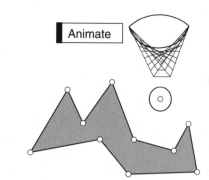

20. Using the **Selection Arrow** tool, click in a blank space to deselect objects.

21. Click on the center point of your ball and go to the Edit menu. Choose **Split Point From Arc.**

22. While the center of the ball is still selected, click on the polygon interior to select it. Go to the Edit menu and choose **Merge Point To Polygon Interior.**

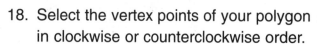
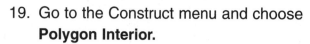
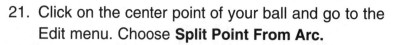

Geometry Activities for Middle School Students with The Geometer's Sketchpad
©2004 Key Curriculum Press

23. Click on your Animation button again. Watch your ball bounce around the polygon. Click once on the Animation button to stop the animation.

24. Click in a blank space to deselect objects. Select the polygon interior and all the sides and points that define the polygon. Go to the Display menu and choose **Hide Objects.**

25. You can construct the circle interior and hide the center point of the ball if you wish. Click on the Animation button again.

26. Using the **Text** tool $\boxed{A}$, double-click to create a text box at the top of your screen.

27. Type your name(s) inside the box.

Gina and Brittany

Summary

In this tour, you have learned to

- Construct an arc and animate a circle (the ball) along the arc
- Animate a circle (the ball) along a polygon interior
- Merge and split points from objects

Animation—Tour 4 (Advanced Animation Techniques)

In this tour, you will learn more techniques of animation in Sketchpad.

1. Go to the "Fish" page of the sketch **Animation.gsp.** The sketch should look similar to the figure below when you open it. You can also create a new sketch and construct the fish and bird yourself if you wish.

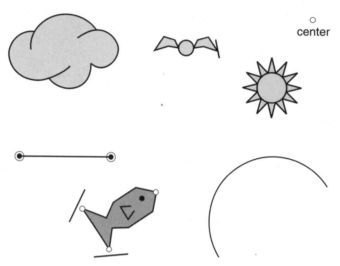

center

First you will animate the fish to make it appear to swim and jump upstream like a salmon.

2. Using the **Selection Arrow** tool ⬚, click on the arc. Go to the Construct menu and choose **Point On Arc.** Drag this point toward the upper-right end of the arc.

3. Click in a blank space to deselect objects. Then select the point at the tip of the mouth on the fish and select the point on your arc. Go to the Transform menu and choose **Mark Vector.**

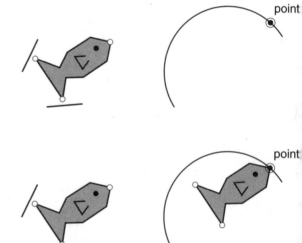

point

point

4. Using a selection marquee, select all of your fish but *not* the arc *or* the two segments at the tail of the fish. Go to the Transform menu and choose **Translate.** In the dialog box, choose **Marked Translation Vector** and then click Translate. You should see a new fish appear that is exactly the distance and direction of the vector from the original fish.

5. Click in a blank space to deselect objects. Click on one of the points at the tip of the fish's tail and select the segment closest to that point. Go to the Edit menu and choose **Merge Point To Segment.**

6. Click in a blank space to deselect objects. Click on the point on the other side of the tail and then click on the segment closest to that point. Go to the Edit menu and choose **Merge Point To Segment.** Click in a blank space to deselect objects.

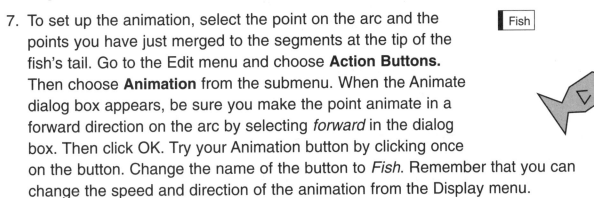

7. To set up the animation, select the point on the arc and the points you have just merged to the segments at the tip of the fish's tail. Go to the Edit menu and choose **Action Buttons.** Then choose **Animation** from the submenu. When the Animate dialog box appears, be sure you make the point animate in a forward direction on the arc by selecting *forward* in the dialog box. Then click OK. Try your Animation button by clicking once on the button. Change the name of the button to *Fish*. Remember that you can change the speed and direction of the animation from the Display menu.

8. Click in a blank space to deselect objects. Hide the original fish and the arc by selecting them and then choosing **Hide Objects** from the Display menu. Try your Animation button again.

Next you will dilate your fish by a fixed ratio to create a smaller fish that also moves, using the same Animation button. (If you just copy and paste the first fish, the new image won't move. But if you create the image by transformations, the image will move just like the one you created first.)

9. Click in a blank space to deselect objects. Click on the point called **center** at the top of the sketch. Go to the Transform menu and choose **Mark Center.**

10. Select the new fish, go to the Transform menu, and choose **Dilate.** When the Dilate dialog box appears, enter 2 in the top (numerator) box and 3 in the bottom (denominator) box. Then click Dilate. You should see a new fish appear that is two-thirds the size of the first fish. Click in a blank space to deselect objects. Click on the Animation button again to see both fish move. Notice that the new fish always remains two-thirds as large as the first fish you created, even during animation. This is because you dilated by a fixed ratio. Click on the Animation button to stop the animation.

Now you will move an object (the bird) so that the new image changes size during the animation.

11. Select the horizontal segment that is drawn in the lower-left part of the sketch. Go to the Construct menu and choose **Point On Segment.**

    You will set up the animation for your bird before you dilate it.

12. Select the new point on the segment and the point on the tip of the wing of the bird. Go to the Edit menu. Choose **Action Buttons** and choose **Animation** from the submenu. For the direction, choose *bidirectional* in the dialog box. Click OK. Also change the name of the button to *Bird*. You may vary the speed now or later if you wish.

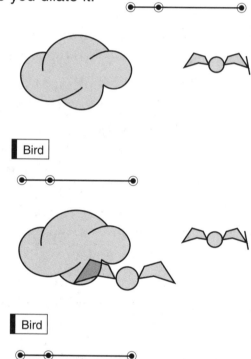

13. Click on the *Bird* button to watch the points move back and forth along the segments on which they are constructed (or merged). The bird's wings move up and down, but the bird stays in one place in the sketch.

Now you will dilate the bird and have it move across the screen so that it gets larger as it seems to fly close to you and smaller as it seems to travel away from you.

14. Click in a blank space to deselect objects. Click on the horizontal segment (not the point on the segment or the two endpoints of the segment). Go to the Display menu and choose **Hide Segment.** Leave the points at the endpoints of the segment and the point in the middle of the segment still showing.

15. Now click on the segment and the point at the tip of the bird's wing. Go to the Display menu and choose **Hide Objects.**

16. Click in a blank space to deselect objects. Click on the left endpoint of the segment you just hid and the point in the middle that was constructed on the segment. Go to the Construct menu and choose **Construct Segment.**

17. Click in a blank space to deselect objects. Click on the right endpoint of the segment and the point in the middle that was constructed on the segment. Go to the Construct menu and choose **Construct Segment.**

18. Click in a blank space to deselect objects. You have constructed two new segments. Click on the left segment and then on the right segment (not the points). Go to the Transform menu and choose **Mark Segment Ratio.**

19. Click in a blank space to deselect objects. Click on the point called **center.** Go to the Transform menu and choose **Mark Center.**

20. Select the bird (drag a marquee around it). Go to the Transform menu and choose **Dilate.** When the Dilate dialog box appears, choose **By Marked Ratio.** Then click Dilate.

21. You should see a new bird appear in your sketch. Click on your *Bird* button again to see the bird get bigger as it travels to the left in the sketch and smaller as it travels back to the right (closer to **center**) in the sketch. The bird gets larger and smaller because the marked ratio is constantly changing as the point moves along the original segment.

22. Click in a blank space to deselect objects. Select the original bird and the horizontal segments and points used to set up the ratio. Go to the Display menu and choose **Hide Objects.**

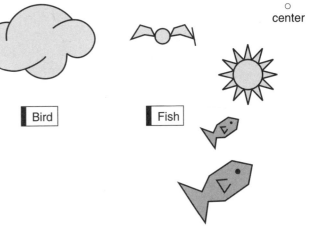

23. Click on both Animation buttons to see the fish swim and the bird fly! Add waves or other details to the sketch if you wish.

24. Click on the **Text** tool ⒜ and double-click at the top of your screen to create a text box.

25. Type your name(s) inside the box.

Summary

In this tour, you have learned to
- Translate an object by a marked vector and then animate the transformed object
- Dilate an animated object by a fixed ratio
- Dilate an object by a marked ratio and animate that object

POINTS, LINES, AND ANGLES

Kyle

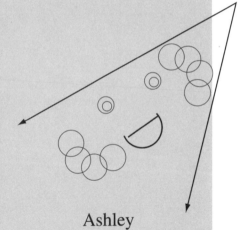

Ashley

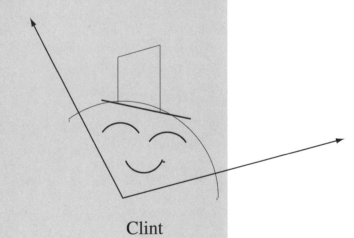

Clint

Commentary

This unit is especially suitable for students who are encountering for the first time the concepts about lines and angles presented in the activities. Formulating their own definitions or lists of characteristics for these concepts not only gives the students ownership of their work, but also enables them to remember the concepts much better.

For many groups of students, it will be appropriate to present some of the activities in this unit as teacher- or student-led demonstrations rather than as independent explorations by each child. This is true both for groups first encountering these topics mathematically and for groups who are already familiar with the topics but who need a quick review. Of course, you must decide which activities and formats best meet the skill levels and needs of a particular group.

Pesky Points helps students understand how points function in the Sketchpad program. This introduction is very important for all students, regardless of their mathematical background, unless they have previous experience with Sketchpad. This is one of the activities that may best serve your students' needs when done as a teacher demonstration; in this case, you can use the student activity sheet as a checklist to ensure that you explain the ways points function with Sketchpad. You may want the students to choose **Auto Show Label for Points** in **Preferences** under the Edit menu as they begin this activity. They should understand the following characteristics of points:

- Points constructed as free points can be dragged anywhere in the sketch.

- A point constructed at the intersection of two objects may drag the objects for which it is an intersection point.

- A point constructed as a point on an object can be dragged anywhere along or around the object but will not drag the object itself and cannot be dragged off the object.

- When you use the **Segment, Ray, Line,** or **Compass** tool, two control points appear as you construct these objects. These points will change the orientation of the object and, in the case of a segment or a circle, also control the size of the object on which they are constructed.

A Point of Interest is designed to lead students to discover that there are an infinite number of points equidistant from two given points. This activity also serves as an exploratory introduction to tracing a locus of a point and requires very little technical expertise.

Because the study of points, lines, and angles usually appears early in the middle school geometry curriculum, most students doing the three **Exploring Angles** activities will be new to Sketchpad. Because of this, the teacher demonstration needs to be done slowly and thoroughly and may require repetition or additional examples for some groups of students. Keep in mind that for many beginners in dealing with angles, the orientation of an angle is a stumbling block unless this characteristic is addressed very early. Students readily accept that an angle can "face any direction" unless they have measured a large number of angles all oriented in the same direction before they are exposed to one turned a different way. Be sure that students drag to form the angles listed in each section of the activity. Repeating the process helps develop confidence in their Sketchpad skills as well as improve their memory for how to perform the maneuver.

In **Exploring Angles,** the page "Angles 2" of the sketch **Angles.gsp** is not dynamic, so students can stay focused on target concepts. At this beginning level, the sketch provides practice in visual recognition of types of angles and in using Sketchpad.

For **Exploring Special Pairs of Angles,** we have found that the most important things to keep in mind during the teacher demonstration are essentially the same as those for **Exploring Angles.** Remembering that the students are

Sketchpad beginners as well as newcomers to the mathematical concepts helps ensure the success of the activity. The continual updating of measures by Sketchpad provides much of the impact of this demonstration. In our classroom, this feature of Sketchpad has convinced more students that some things simply are *always* true than has the text or all our proclamations! You will have allies: Listen for one student to say to another, "It must happen all the time. We've tried all the ways there are, and it always turns out the same. Don't you see those numbers on the screen?"

Exploring Angles Formed by Parallel Lines and a Transversal is one of the activities that most clearly demonstrates the power of Sketchpad. So many examples appear in such a short time that students quickly grasp a concept that is traditionally time-consuming and tricky to teach. Students repeatedly refer to this activity later in the year: "Don't you remember? Those angles are always congruent, like we did with Sketchpad when we dragged that transversal, you remember."

Interesting Angles has often surprised us. Students who we suspected might have trouble have often enjoyed this project the most: kids see it as a puzzle. The inevitable experimentation builds confidence with Sketchpad, and kids are often eager to show off unique solutions. Promoting "illustrations" like those at the top of the instructions adds to the fun. Directions are included in Instructions for Teacher Demonstrations later in these notes.

Name Angles has been a great motivator for our kids. They love to show their creations to the class. Having classmates guess the measure of the angles in each of the sketches, followed up by measuring with Sketchpad or a protractor, is a fun way to practice, too.

Angle Puzzle is considerably more difficult than the other activities. Most likely, it will be used best as a reinforcement or extension at a later time or with more knowledgeable groups.

Certainly, **Angle Puzzle** should be done in groups, since students working alone may get frustrated with it. It is an especially good activity when you are trying to establish the value of cooperative learning, because different individuals invariably notice different details that help unravel the "mystery" for the group. We have found it effective to let students work alone at first, then to pair them with a partner after a short time, and finally to combine two pairs a little later.

Angle Puzzle is not dynamic and, in fact, does not require the use of Sketchpad at all; however, we included it because it involves valuable synthesis and application. It also provides an alternative assessment instrument that requires substantial application of the concepts presented in the activities in this unit. The Sketchpad component, of course, is the Challenge at the end. Having students work each other's Challenges is a must; furthermore, students should view their first attempts only as a draft, and they should gain insight from initial errors.

Students should be warned to read the directions for **Sharp Shooter** extremely carefully. The kids to whom this project appeals especially enjoy the portion in which the ball must bounce off two walls, but it is too difficult for some middle schoolers. Knowledge of reflections enhances this project and suggests alternative solutions.

The Sketchpad skills required by **Creating a Sketchpad Clock** may cause you to deem it more appropriate at some later point in the year. For some reason, the notion of creating an accurate model of a clock comes up with almost every new group of students who work with Sketchpad, but they really need knowledge of animation, reflection, dilation, and rotation before they can successfully create a "working" model. Students will persevere and take great pride in demonstrating their final product for their classmates. This project is a terrific "teaser" to mention early in the year and revisit after students have done transformations. Of course, some kids could explore transformations on their own using the activities in Unit 6 and then try the project if you feel it is appropriate.

Referring to the Wrap-Up for this unit, we would like to emphasize an observation: Although the *always, sometimes, never* format is a little too difficult for some middle school kids, our experience is that many kids improve dramatically after practice with this format and that the understanding gained is clearly more than that accomplished by true-false questions. We would encourage you to try the format several times before becoming discouraged.

Prerequisite Mathematical Terms and Concepts

- *point, line, ray, segment, endpoint*
- measuring angles

Recommended Sketchpad Proficiency

- Basic knowledge of the freehand tools; beginner-level Sketchpad proficiency.

- Use of the Points, Lines, and Angles Quick Reference Guide (found at the end of this unit) is suggested.

- Doing Tours 1 and 2 would be beneficial (see Tours unit).

Essential Vocabulary

Acute angle—any angle measuring less than 90° and greater than 0°

Alternate exterior angles—a pair of angles formed by parallel lines and a transversal where both angles are outside the parallel lines but on opposite sides of the transversal

Alternate interior angles—a pair of angles formed by parallel lines and a transversal where both angles are inside the parallel lines but on opposite sides of the transversal

Angle—two rays with a common endpoint; usually named by three letters with the vertex label as the middle letter

Complementary angles—a pair of angles whose measures total 90°

Corresponding angles—a pair of angles formed by parallel lines and a transversal where one angle is outside the parallel lines and the other is inside, and both angles are on the same side of the transversal

Obtuse angle—any angle measuring greater than 90° and less than 180°

Parallel lines—two or more lines in a plane that never intersect

Right angle—any angle measuring exactly 90°

Straight angle—any angle measuring exactly 180°

Supplementary angles—a pair of angles whose measures total 180°

Transversal—a line that intersects two lines to form eight angles

Vertical angles—a pair of angles that are formed by a pair of intersecting lines and do not share a side

Instructions for Teacher Demonstrations

In each unit, we have included sketches and guidelines for demonstrations the teacher can use to introduce the material to the whole class before students attempt the various activities independently. They include the introduction of relevant mathematical vocabulary and concepts as well as appropriate Sketchpad skills. Often there are one or two activities that you will feel comfortable assigning to your students with very little guidance beforehand. In this unit, for example, **A Point of Interest** works fine as an exploratory introduction to tracing a locus of a point and requires very little technical expertise.

On the other hand, one or more activities in each unit are designed to maximize guided discovery by the students. For these activities, a careful teacher demonstration will focus the students' attention on targeted mathematical concepts and prevent distractions due to lack of Sketchpad proficiency. In this unit, the activities **Exploring Angles, Exploring Special Pairs of Angles,** and **Exploring Angles Formed by Parallel Lines and a Transversal** are designed to follow such a demonstration. Instructions are included later in these notes. Of course, you may want to use portions or adaptations of the demonstrations before other activities; certainly you will want to preview activities to be sure they are appropriate for the mathematical and Sketchpad skill levels of your students. Even with careful demonstrations, many students will forget one or more steps when they try something for the first time, for example, measuring an angle at the computer. You need to show several examples and then, at the close of the teacher demonstration, have a student sit at the computer while another student gives verbal instructions.

We find it very valuable to solicit student suggestions during the demonstrations. In the parallel lines demonstrations, for example, a student invariably suggests first using the freehand **Segment** ◻ or **Line** tool ◻ to construct a line parallel to a given line. Errors like this stimulate thought, result in lively class discussion, and provide many opportunities for guided discovery.

You may find the Points, Lines, and Angles Quick Reference Guide (at the end of this unit) helpful in preparing for the teacher demonstrations.

Exploring Angles

Introducing Points, Segments, Rays, and Lines

Open a new sketch. Use the freehand tools to demonstrate and discuss *point, segment, ray,* and *line*.

- Construct free points.
- Construct and drag a segment. (Discuss endpoints.)
- Construct and drag a ray. (Discuss the endpoint and other control point.)
- Construct and drag a line. (Discuss the two control points.)

Introducing Angles

1. Open a new sketch. Use the **Segment** ◻ and **Ray** tools ◻ to construct several angles. Demonstrate the following Sketchpad skills:

   - Construct an angle using the **Segment** tool ◻.
   - Construct an angle using the **Ray** tool ◻.
   - Measure both angles. (Be sure you orient the angles in several different directions, for example, as ∠ and ∠. Also emphasize that the vertex must be the middle point selected when measuring.)

2. Point out to students that angles in some sketches in this unit will appear as "textbook angles," with arrows at the ends of segments to represent rays. Others will appear with rays that go off the sketch, implying that the rays continue indefinitely in one direction.

3. Use the same sketch to show and discuss acute, obtuse, and right angles.

4. Using **PLA Demos.gsp**, discuss and demonstrate the interior and exterior of an angle. Discuss and construct points on the angle, in the interior of the angle, and in the exterior of the angle.

Exploring Special Pairs of Angles

1. Review *angles* and naming angles.

2. Demonstrate the following Sketchpad skills using the "PLA Demo 2" page of the sketch **PLA Demos.gsp**.

- Drag point **A**, **B**, **C**, or **D** using the **Selection Arrow** tool ⬆. Each of these points changes the angle measure or orientation of the angle when dragged.

- Drag any of the points at the end of the arrows to show that the measure of the angle does not depend on the length of the indicated ray. (Remind students that the ray should be thought of as having infinite length.)

- Make observations from displayed measures (for example, $m\angle ABD + m\angle DBC$ always equals $m\angle ABC$).

3. Discuss the angles formed by intersecting lines. Demonstrate the following Sketchpad skills using the "PLA Demo 3" page of the sketch **PLA Demos.gsp.**

   - Display the measure of any angle. Do not display the measures of all four angles, since students will be doing this in the activity.

   - Drag point **S** or **B** to change the measures of the angles.

Exploring Angles Formed by Parallel Lines and a Transversal

1. Discuss the angles formed by a transversal intersecting two lines. Present the following concepts using the "PLA Demo 4" page of the sketch **PLA Demos.gsp:** *transversal, corresponding angles, alternate interior angles,* and *alternate exterior angles.*

2. Discuss the relationship between the various angles formed using the "PLA Demo 4" page of the sketch **PLA Demos.gsp.**

   - Measure some of the angles within the figure.

   - Demonstrate how the orientation of the lines and the measures of the angles change as you drag point **A**, **B**, or **D**.

   - Demonstrate how the orientation of the transversal and the measures of the angles change as you drag point **N**.

Note: For some classes, it will be more appropriate to do **Exploring Angles Formed by Parallel Lines and a Transversal** totally as a teacher demonstration. If you do so, you may want to demonstrate not only with the "PLA Demo 4" page of the sketch **PLA Demos.gsp** but also with the sketch **Parallel.gsp.**

Writing Prompts

Ask students to choose a topic below and to write a short paper, including sketches created with Sketchpad.

- Angles Party (and the Special Pairs Who Attend)

- Important Points About Angles

- Points, Lines, and Angles—The Basics of Geometry

- Taking a Geometric Walk (Observing Lines and Angles in My Neighborhood)

Examples of Student Work

| Name Angles Project | Interesting Angles Project |

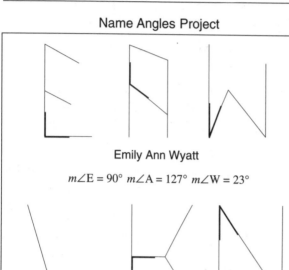

Emily Ann Wyatt

$m\angle E = 90°$ $m\angle A = 127°$ $m\angle W = 23°$

Laura Kathryn Nolin

$m\angle L = 107°$ $m\angle K = 90°$ $m\angle N = 35°$

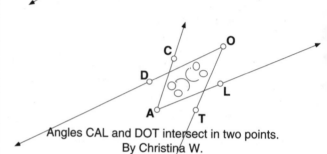

Angles DAN and FAY intersect in one point.
By Matt N.

Angles CAL and DOT intersect in two points.
By Christina W.

Answers for Exploring Angles Activity

Orientation of these angles will vary.

2. a. 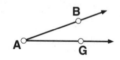 b.   c.

d.  e.   f.

3. a. 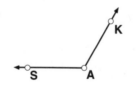 b. 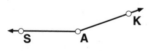 c.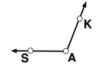

d. 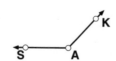 e. 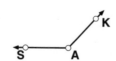 f.

4. a.   b.

5. a. 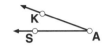   b.

7. acute; 70°

8. a. acute; 60°   b. obtuse; 155°   c. acute; 45°
    d. obtuse; 95°   e. acute; 40°   f. right; 90°
    g. obtuse; 135°   h. right; 90°   i. acute; 20°
    j. right; 90°

Answers for Exploring Special Pairs of Angles Activity

2. The sum equals 90°.   3. two angles whose sum is 90°
5. The sum equals 180°.   6. two angles whose sum is 180°
9. They are always equal.   10. They are always equal.
11. A pair of vertical angles have equal measures.
12. supplementary; supplementary
13. You need to know only one angle measure. If you know one angle, it is equal to
    one of the angles and supplementary to the other two angles.

Answers for Exploring Angles Formed by Parallel Lines and a Transversal Activity

2. They are equal in measure.
3. a. ∠EOR, ∠HEM = ∠EOR   b. ∠RON, ∠MEO = ∠RON
    c. ∠YON, ∠XEO = ∠YON
4. equal; equal in measure
5. They are equal in measure.
6. ∠YEO; ∠EOR. Their sum is 180°.
7. They are equal; equal.
8. They have equal measures.
9. ∠HEX; ∠RON. They are equal.
10. They are equal; equal in measure.

Answers for Angle Puzzle Project

$m\angle 1 = 130°$ $m\angle 2 = 130°$ $m\angle 3 = 50°$
$m\angle 4 = 30°$ $m\angle 5 = 70°$ $m\angle 6 = 70°$
$m\angle 7 = 60°$ $m\angle 8 = 40°$
$m\angle 9 = 40°$ $m\angle 10 = 50°$

Answers for Points, Lines, and Angles Wrap-Up

1. acute
2. obtuse
3. right
4. acute
5. obtuse
6. acute
7. a. supplementary   b. 155°
8. a. complementary   b. 40°
9. a. vertical   b. 135°
10. a. vertical and complementary   b. 45°
11. a. alternate interior   b. 40°
12. a. corresponding   b. 130°
13. a. alternate exterior   b. 140°
14. a. corresponding   b. 60°
15. sometimes
16. sometimes
17. sometimes
18. always
19. never
20. sometimes

Pesky Points

Because Sketchpad is a dynamic tool, points will behave differently depending on how they are constructed. This activity helps you explore such points.

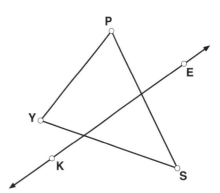

1. Open the sketch **Points.gsp**.

2. Using the **Point** tool , click to create a point somewhere in the sketch so that it does not touch any of the objects already in the sketch. This point will probably be labeled point **A**. If the label does not appear when you create the point, click on the point using the **Text** tool A.

3. Using the **Selection Arrow** tool, click in a blank space to deselect objects.

4. Click on ⃡EK and P̄S̄ with the **Selection Arrow** tool to select them (don't click on the points on the line or the points on the segment). Go to the Construct menu and choose **Intersection**. This new point will probably be labeled point **B**. Click in a blank space to deselect objects.

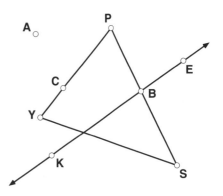

5. Click on P̄Ȳ (not on the points **P** and **Y**). Go to the Construct menu and choose **Point On Segment**. This new point will probably be labeled point **C**.

Your sketch probably looks similar to the one above. Now you will experiment with the way different points behave.

6. Use the **Selection Arrow** tool to drag point **A**. Describe the effects on the figure.

_____

_____

_____

7. Use the **Selection Arrow** tool to drag point **C**. Describe the effects on the figure. Did points **A** and **C** behave in the same manner? Explain. _____

_____

_____

8. Use the **Selection Arrow** tool to drag point **B**. Describe the effects on the figure. Is the behavior of point **B** like that of point **A** or **C**? Explain. _____

_____

_____

9. Use the **Selection Arrow** tool to drag point **E**. Describe the effects on the figure. What happens to point **B** when you drag point **E** so that the line no longer crosses the triangle? _____

_____

_____

10. Explain why you think the different points behaved differently. _____

_____

_____

11. Open a new sketch.

12. Use the **Compass** tool to construct a circle in your sketch.

13. Use the **Selection Arrow** tool to drag the center of your circle. What happens to the circle? _____

_____

_____

14. Now drag the point on the circle. What happens? _____

_____

_____

15. Click on the circle to select it (don't select the center point or the point on the circle). Go to the Construct menu and choose **Point On Circle** to construct another point on the circle. Drag this point. Describe what happens. _____

_____

_____

16. Explain why you think the different points behaved differently. _____

_____

_____

Geometry Activities for Middle School Students with The Geometer's Sketchpa
©2004 Key Curriculum Pres

A Point of Interest

If you are given two points, how many points are equidistant (the same distance) from the two given points?

Because Sketchpad is a dynamic tool, points can be traced (can leave a path) when animated. This activity helps you find points that are equidistant from two given points and answer the question above.

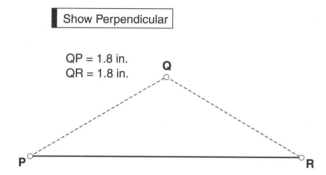

Show Perpendicular

QP = 1.8 in.
QR = 1.8 in.

1. Open the sketch **Equidistant.gsp.** Notice that the distances between points **Q** and **P** and points **Q** and **R** are displayed in the sketch. As you can see, point **Q** is equidistant from points **P** and **R**.

2. Carefully drag point **Q** so that the distances change, but try to keep the distances as close to equal as you can. Is there more than one position where point **Q** is equidistant from points **P** and **R**? _____

3. Use the **Selection Arrow** tool ⬆ and click the *Show Perpendicular* button in your sketch. Move point **Q** along the perpendicular. Notice the distances as they are updated on your screen. Are there positions besides the one where point **Q** started that are equidistant from points **P** and **R**? _____

4. Click on the *Move Q to Perpendicular* button and drag point **Q** along the perpendicular. In how many positions along the perpendicular is point **Q** equidistant to points **P** and **R**? _____

5. Click the *Animate Point* button and observe the measurements.

6. Based on your observations, answer the question at the beginning of this activity.

_____

_____

Exploring Angles

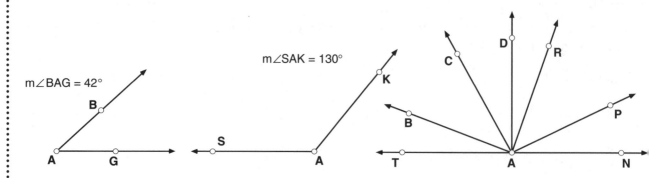

Two rays with a common endpoint form an angle. Use Sketchpad to explore angles.

1. Open the sketch **Angles.gsp** and select the "Angles 1" page.

2. Notice ∠**BAG**. It is an *acute angle* (an angle with measure less than 90°). For each measure listed below, drag either **B** or **G** to observe the angle and make a sketch of your result.

   a. 20°

   b. 45°

   c. 82.5°

   d. 5°

   e. 35.5°

   f. 65°

3. Notice ∠**SAK**. It is an *obtuse angle* (an angle with measure between 90° and 180°). For each measure listed below, drag **S** or **K** to observe the angle and make a sketch of your result.

   a. 120°

   b. 160°

   c. 95°

   d. 175.4°

   e. 135°

   f. 110.7°

4. Of course, you can drag ∠**SAK** to make it an acute angle as well. Drag **S** or **K** to observe an angle with each measure listed below and make a sketch of your result.

   a. 20°

   b. 45°

5. A *right angle* measures exactly 90°. Drag to make ∠**BAG** and ∠**SAK** right angles. Sketch your results below.

   a. *m*∠**BAG** = 90° _____

   b. *m*∠**SAK** = 90° _____

6. Go to the page "Angles 2."

7. To measure an angle in Sketchpad, do the following steps:

   • Click on three points: a point on either side, the vertex, and the point on the other side, in clockwise or counterclockwise order. Be sure the vertex is the middle point selected.

   • Go to the Measure menu and choose **Angle.** You should see the measure of the angle appear on the screen.

   What kind of angle is ∠**RAN** (*acute, right,* or *obtuse*)? _____

   What is the measure of ∠**RAN**? _____

   You should have found *m*∠**RAN** = 70°, which means it is an acute angle.

8. For each angle listed below, do the following:

   • Write whether you think it is *acute, right,* or *obtuse.*

   • Estimate the measure of the angle.

   • Use Sketchpad to measure the angle and record its actual measure.

   • Change your answer for the kind of angle, if necessary.

	Angle	Acute, Right, or Obtuse	Estimated Measure	Actual Measure
a.	∠CAT			
b.	∠PAT			
c.	∠RAP			
d.	∠CAP			
e.	∠CAB			
f.	∠DAN			
g.	∠BAP			
h.	∠TAD			
i.	∠RAD			
j.	∠BAR			

Exploring Special Pairs of Angles

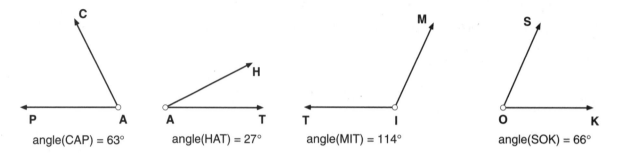

angle(CAP) = 63°   angle(HAT) = 27°   angle(MIT) = 114°   angle(SOK) = 66°

In geometry, you study several special kinds of pairs of angles. Use Sketchpad to explore some of these pairs.

1. Open the sketch **Pairs.gsp** and go to the "Pairs 1" page.

2. Notice ∠**CAP** and ∠**HAT**. They are *complementary angles.* As you drag point **X**, the angles will remain complementary. What do you notice about the sum of their measures? _____

_____

3. Use your observation from step 2 to define complementary angles.

4. Go to the "Pairs 2" page.

5. Notice ∠**MIT** and ∠**SOK**. They are *supplementary angles.* As you drag point **G**, the angles will remain supplementary. What do you notice about the sum of their measures? _____

_____

6. Use your observation from step 5 to define supplementary angles.

_____

7. Go to the "Pairs 3" page.

8. Notice that four angles are formed by a pair of intersecting lines. In this sketch, line **BK** intersects line **GS** to form the following angles: ∠**BAG**, ∠**SAK**, ∠**BAS**, and ∠**GAK**.

9. ∠**SAK** and ∠**BAG** are a pair of *vertical angles.* How do the measures of the angles compare? _____

_____

       Geometry Activities for Middle School Students with The Geometer's Sketchpad
©2004 Key Curriculum Press

10. ∠**BAS** and ∠**GAK** are also vertical angles. How do their measures compare?

    _____

11. Drag points **S** and **B**. As you drag, the pairs of angles remain vertical angles. What conclusion can you draw about the measures of any pair of vertical angles? _____

    _____

12. What kind of angles are ∠**BAS** and ∠**SAK**? _____

    What kind of angles are ∠**BAG** and ∠**GAK**? _____

13. From what you now know about vertical and supplementary angles, answer the following question: When two lines intersect, four angles are formed. How many angle measures would you need to know before you could name the measures of all the angles? _____

    Draw an example and write a short explanation to show how to do this.

    _____

    _____

    _____

    _____

    _____

    _____

    _____

    _____

Exploring Angles Formed by
Parallel Lines and a Transversal

When parallel lines are intersected by a third line, called a *transversal,* there are certain relationships among the angles formed. Use Sketchpad to explore these relationships.

1. Open the sketch **Parallel.gsp.**

2. Find ∠**HEX** and ∠**EOY**. They are a pair of *corresponding angles.* How do their measures compare? _____

3. For each angle given below, list its corresponding angle and tell how the measures compare.

   a. ∠**HEM** _____

   b. ∠**MEO** _____

   c. ∠**XEO** _____

4. Drag point **N** slowly and notice the measures of each pair of corresponding angles. How do their measures always compare? _____

   _____

   Complete the following statement: If two parallel lines are cut by a transversal, then the corresponding angles are _____.

5. Find ∠**MEO** and ∠**EOY**. They are a pair of *alternate interior angles.* How do their measures compare? _____

6. Name the other pair of alternate interior angles in the sketch: _____ and _____. How do their measures compare? _____

   _____

Geometry Activities for Middle School Students with The Geometer's Sketchpad
©2004 Key Curriculum Press

7. Drag point **N** slowly and notice the measures of both pairs of alternate interior angles. How do their measures compare? _____
Complete the following statement: If two parallel lines are cut by a transversal, then the alternate interior angles are _____.

8. Find ∠**HEM** and ∠**YON**. They are a pair of alternate exterior angles. How do their measures compare? _____

9. Name the other pair of alternate exterior angles in the sketch:
_____ and _____. How do their measures compare?

_____

10. Drag point **N** slowly and notice the measures of both pairs of alternate exterior angles. How do their measures always compare? _____

_____

Complete the following statement: If two parallel lines are cut by a transversal, then the alternate exterior angles are _____

_____.

Interesting Angles

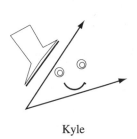

Kyle

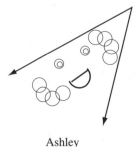

Ashley

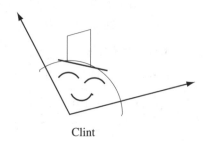

Clint

1. Open a new sketch.

   Use Sketchpad to construct the following:

   a. a pair of angles that intersect at one point

   b. a pair of angles that intersect at two points

   c. a pair of angles that intersect at three points

   d. a pair of angles that intersect at four points

   e. a pair of angles that intersect at an infinite number of points

   f. a pair of angles that intersect at any other number of points

2. If you used the **Segment** tool ⧄ to construct your angles and wish to make arrowheads at the ends of the segments, you may do the following:

   a. Go to the **Sketchpad** folder and open the **Samples** folder.

   b. Open the **Custom Tools** folder.

   c. Open the **Appearance Tools.gsp** sketch.

   d. Leave **Appearance Tools.gsp** open and return to your sketch.

   e. Click on the **Custom** tool ▶: (or ▶▶) and select **Appearance Tools.gsp**. (*Note:* This option will only be available when the sketch **Appearance Tools.gsp** is open.)

   f. Choose **Arrowhead(Open)** from the Custom Tools menu.

   g. Start at the vertex of each angle and drag along one segment to the point where you wish to place the arrowhead. Repeat on the other segment of the angle.

3. Put your name in the sketch and print out a copy to hand in.

Challenge: In how many points can three angles intersect? Use Sketchpad to investigate.

Name Angles

1. Open a new sketch.

2. Use the **Segment** tool ⬜ to write your initials in the sketch.

3. Display the measures of three angles in your sketch. Try to show one acute, one obtuse, and one right angle, if possible.

Example:

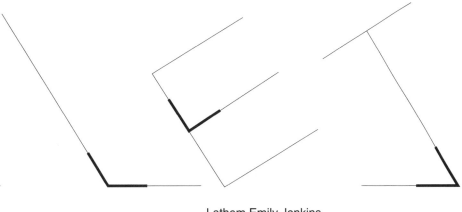

Lathem Emily Jenkins

L's angle measure = 122°   **E**'s angle measure = 90°   **J**'s angle measure = 58°

4. Put your name(s) in the sketch and print out a copy to hand in.

Angle Puzzle

1. Using only the information you are given in the drawing below, work with the students in your group to find the measure of each numbered angle.

2. Use what you know about the measures of special pairs of angles and angles formed by parallel lines and a transversal to help you. Also, remember that the sum of the angles of any triangle is 180°.

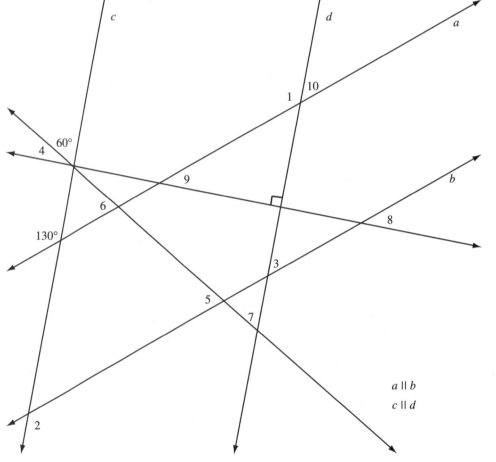

a ∥ b
c ∥ d

m∠1 = _____   m∠2 = _____   m∠3 = _____   m∠4 = _____

m∠5 = _____   m∠6 = _____   m∠7 = _____   m∠8 = _____

m∠9 = _____   m∠10 = _____

Challenge: Use Sketchpad to design your own Angle Puzzle. You must be careful to construct parallel lines that will stay parallel. Also, try only a few angles at first! Have another student try your first draft, and don't be surprised if you have to revise.

Geometry Activities for Middle School Students with The Geometer's Sketchpad
©2004 Key Curriculum Press

Sharp Shooter

The figure below is a scale drawing of a pool table, with points **C**, **D**, and **F** representing balls. Points **T**, **A**, **B**, **L**, **E**, and **Q** represent pockets. Suppose you want the ball to bounce off one of the sides of the pool table and roll into one of the pockets. Where on the table would you aim for the ball to strike? Remember that the path of a ball must make equal angles with a side of the pool table to model or simulate a real pool ball, as shown in the figure.

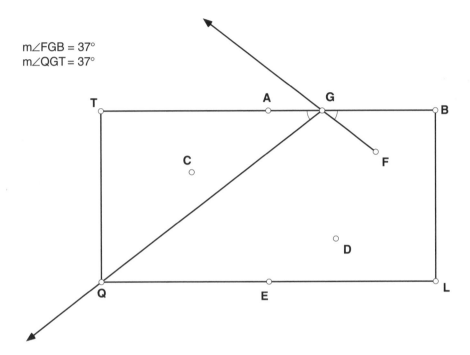

m∠FGB = 37°
m∠QGT = 37°

1. Open the sketch **Pool.gsp**.

2. Use the **Ray** tool ☑ to construct a path for one of the balls. The ball must be the endpoint of your ray, and the other control point must be constructed on the side at which you decide to aim. Construct a second ray with the intersection point of the first ray and the side as its endpoint and the other control point the pocket for which you are aiming. Measure the angles made by the path of the ball and the side of the pool table. Drag the point on the side to adjust the measures of the angles until they are congruent.

3. Print out a copy with your results.

4. Repeat this for the other two balls.

5. Go to the Edit menu and choose **Undo** until you see the original pool table on the screen. This time, try to find the path of a ball that bounces off two sides and then enters a pocket.

Creating a Sketchpad Clock

1. Open a new sketch and create an accurate model of a clock.

2. Display correct measures for any time of day.

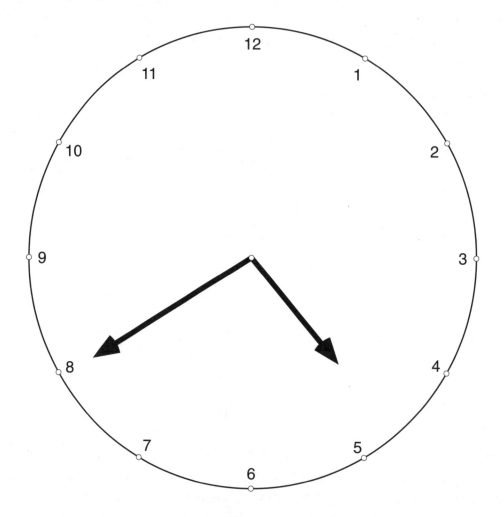

angle between hands measures 100°

Challenge: Animate the hands of your clock so that they move just like the hands of a real clock. Make sure the hands rotate clockwise.

1. Investigate how runways are numbered at airports. Use Sketchpad to illustrate how angles determine the numbers and what they mean to pilots.

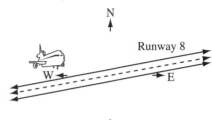

2. Investigate how angles are used in celestial navigation. Use Sketchpad to create a sketch that illustrates this means of determining your position.

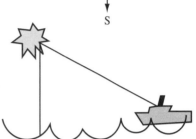

3. Use Sketchpad to construct three lines intersecting at a single point to form six angles. Construct a point on each ray that doesn't already have a point on it. Notice special pairs of angles formed. Experiment to discover how many angle measures you would need to know in order to find the rest.

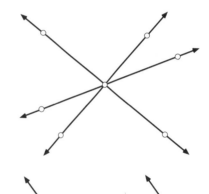

4. Investigate the relationship between the measures of pairs of consecutive interior angles formed by a pair of parallel lines and a transversal. Also, investigate the relationship between the measures of pairs of consecutive exterior angles formed by a pair of parallel lines and a transversal.

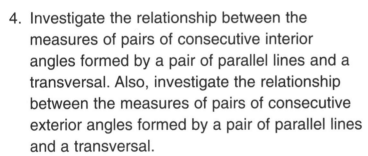

5. Explore the relationship between the measures of an exterior angle of a triangle and the two remote (nonadjacent) interior angles. Then investigate the relationship between the measures of an exterior angle of a quadrilateral and the three nonadjacent interior angles.

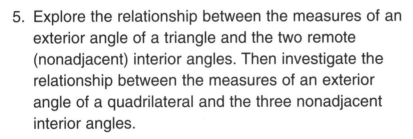

6. Explore with diagonals in polygons to find a pattern for the maximum number of intersection points of the diagonals of a convex polygon.

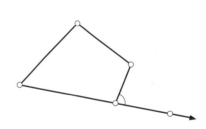

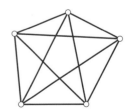

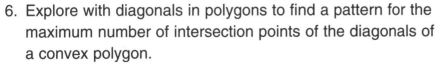

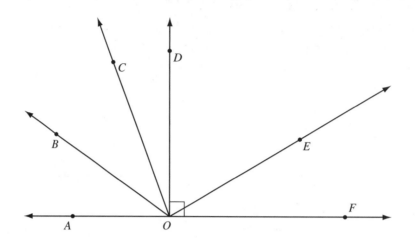

Tell whether each angle listed below is acute, right, or obtuse.

1. ∠COD _____   2. ∠BOE _____

3. ∠DOA _____   4. ∠FOE _____

5. ∠EOA _____   6. ∠AOC _____

For each pair of angles in questions 7–10, (a) identify the pair as complementary, supplementary, or vertical and (b) give the measure of the numbered angle.

7.   8.

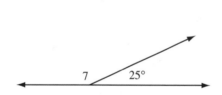   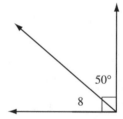

   a. _____   a. _____

   b. _____   b. _____

9.   10.

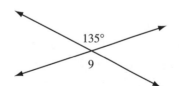   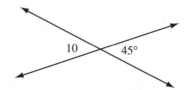

   a. _____   a. _____

   b. _____   b. _____

Geometry Activities for Middle School Students with The Geometer's Sketchpad
©2004 Key Curriculum Press

For each pair of angles in questions 11–14, (a) classify the pair as corresponding angles, alternate interior angles, or alternate exterior angles and (b) give the measure of the numbered angle. For these questions, the two horizontal lines are parallel.

11.

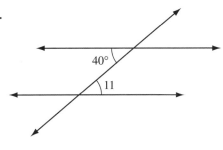

a. _____

b. _____

12.

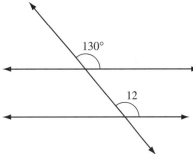

a. _____

b. _____

13.

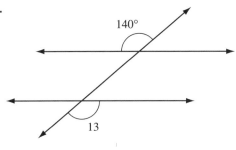

a. _____

b. _____

14.

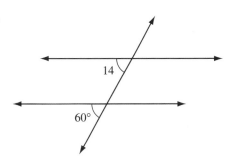

a. _____

b. _____

Write *sometimes, always,* or *never* for each statement in questions 15–20.

15. _____ A pair of angles are vertical and acute.

16. _____ Alternate interior angles formed by parallel lines and a transversal are complementary.

17. _____ A pair of angles are vertical and supplementary.

18. _____ Corresponding angles formed by parallel lines and a transversal are congruent.

19. _____ Alternate exterior angles formed by parallel lines and a transversal are vertical angles.

20. _____ One of a pair of supplementary angles is acute and one is obtuse.

To measure an angle (use the **Selection Arrow** tool)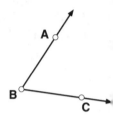

1. Click on the three points that define the angle. (Make sure you click on the vertex second. To measure ∠**B**, click on **A**, **B**, and then **C**, or click on **C**, **B**, and then **A**.)

2. Go to the Measure menu and choose **Angle.**

To construct a segment between two existing points (use the **Selection Arrow** tool)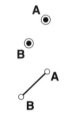

1. Click on the two points.

2. Go to the Construct menu and choose **Segment.**

To construct the point(s) of intersection for two objects (use the **Selection Arrow** tool)

1. Click on the two objects.

2. Go to the Construct menu and choose **Intersections.**

To construct a line parallel to a given line, ray, or segment through a given point (use the **Selection Arrow** tool)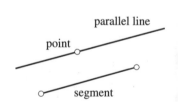

1. Click on the point and the given line, ray, or segment.

2. Go to the Construct menu and choose **Parallel Line.**

To construct a line perpendicular to a given line, ray, or segment through a given point (use the **Selection Arrow** tool)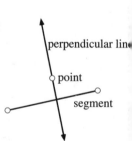

1. Click on the point and the given line, ray, or segment.

2. Go to the Construct menu and choose **Perpendicular Line.**

To display or hide a label (use the **Text** tool)

1. Position the **Text** tool over the object and click once. For a segment, click on the segment itself, not on the endpoints.

2. To hide the label, click on the object again (not on the label).

Geometry Activities for Middle School Students with The Geometer's Sketchpad
©2004 Key Curriculum Press

To move a label (use the **Text** tool $\boxed{\text{A}}$)

1. Click on the label and drag it to any location close to the object.

To change a label name (use the **Text** tool $\boxed{\text{A}}$)

1. Double-click on the label.

2. When the dialog box appears, enter the new name in the Label box.

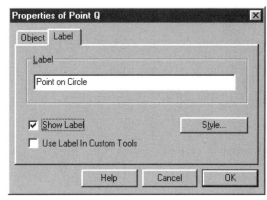

Property Dialog Box (Windows)

To write your name(s) on a sketch and then print (use the **Text** tool $\boxed{\text{A}}$)

1. Double-click in a blank space to make a text box.

2. Type your name(s) in this box.

3. Go to the File menu and choose **Print.**

To create and save a custom tool

1. Use a selection marquee to select your figure. (Make sure all parts are selected.)

2. Click on the **Custom** tool $\boxed{\blacktriangleright\vdots}$ (or $\boxed{\blacktriangleright\!\blacktriangleright}$) and choose **Create New Tool.**

3. In the dialog box, type the name of your new tool. Click OK.

4. To try out your new custom tool, click and hold on the **Custom** tool $\boxed{\blacktriangleright\vdots}$ (or $\boxed{\blacktriangleright\!\blacktriangleright}$) until the menu appears. Choose the new tool.

5. Go to any blank space in your sketch. Click and drag. You should see a new figure. If you wish to alter your new figure, use the **Selection Arrow** tool $\boxed{\text{\textperthousand}}$ and then move the figure or click in any blank space and drag a vertex to change its appearance.

6. You can delete your new figure if you wish before you save your custom tool. All custom tools need to be saved in the **Tool** folder, which is located in the **Sketchpad** folder. Use the **Save As** command under the File menu to save your sketch in this folder. You will need to enter the name of the tool again when the Save As dialog box appears.

Note: Later you can open the sketch containing the custom tool and use your custom tool to create your figure in any sketch. The new figure will have the same defining characteristics as your original construction.

TRIANGLES

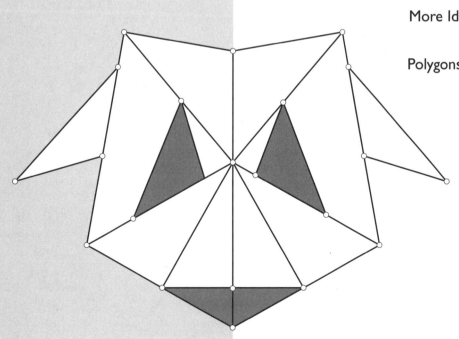

Commentary

The skill levels required by the activities in the Triangles unit probably reflect the widest range of any in this book. The activities and projects range from **Angles** (which is appropriate for students who have little or no experience with triangles) to **Pythagoras Plus** (which is a discovery activity for many mathematics teachers!).

Throughout this unit, you need to emphasize the effects of rounding numbers in general and when using Sketchpad. For example, while using the "Pythagoras 2" page of the sketch **Pythagoras 2.gsp**, where side lengths are displayed to the nearest tenth and angle measures are displayed to the nearest unit, the sketch may display **a** = 3.0, **b** = 4.0, and **c** = 5.0 and yet may display $m\angle$**NOW** as 91°. Preferences are set and saved in the sketches provided with this unit to help minimize the effects of rounding, but students must learn to deal with this reality. As you probably experience in your own classroom, we find that some middle school math students need several reminders of this particular feature!

When your students do **Altitudes,** encourage them to drag angles **H, J,** and **K** to make each of them obtuse or right before formulating their conjectures. For **Area,** you may need to remind some students that Sketchpad will display the area of a polygon if they select the polygon interior and choose Area from the Measure menu. It may be appropriate to show the activity **Angles** as a teacher demonstration whether or not you choose to include the section dealing with exterior angles. The sum of angle measures in a triangle is also covered in **Exploring Properties of Triangles,** so you will want to choose which activity is more appropriate for your students.

Students for whom **Exploring Properties of Triangles** is appropriate may need a detailed teacher demonstration, since most of them have had little experience with either Sketchpad or formal geometry. Also, this activity is likely to be one of the first encounters with Sketchpad for

many students. The portion of the activity that deals with the sum of the angle measures can be a class demonstration for some more experienced groups. For others, it will be primarily a reminder. However, for some beginner groups, the activity will be entirely new; you may want to add a follow-up demonstration by tearing one or more paper triangles and arranging the three angles to form a straight angle to help establish the concept. At the other extreme, the portion of this activity that deals with triangle inequalities, which seem quite obvious to most teachers, seems to surprise even many students who have had a good bit of classroom experience with geometry before encountering Sketchpad. For students at all skill levels, the discovery method Sketchpad affords makes it much easier to remember to test the sum of each pair of sides against the length of the third side to determine whether the triangle is possible. With a textbook or even a chalkboard demonstration, our students in the past nodded when the idea was presented but repeatedly forgot it in follow-up activities or written assessments. This portion of the activity seems a must for groups at all levels.

Before trying **Exploring Types of Triangles,** students need to understand clearly the classification of triangles by sides and by angles; only then can they discover the relationships among the characteristics of triangles as defined by these classifications through practice with the sketches. It was gratifying to hear the discussions between and among pairs as they worked: "Look, you can tell that every equilateral triangle is also isosceles because any two sides you choose are already the same length"; "Of course a right triangle has two acute angles—you have only 90° left for both of them"; and "OK, show me a scalene obtuse triangle, Mr. Smartie!" We have yet to have a group of middle schoolers for whom this activity is not beneficial.

Exploring the Pythagorean Theorem is designed to introduce students to the theorem.

Again, the teacher demonstration plays an important role for most students because the activity incorporates building a table with Sketchpad, a skill most middle school students either have not encountered or do not use often enough to recall without a reminder. With students who have had some exposure to the theorem, it was surprising to us how many of our students assumed the relationship would also exist among the side lengths in nonright triangles. Of course, if you have time constraints, you could split this activity into two parts, but we have encountered misunderstanding among some students when we have rushed or omitted the second half. The informal exposure to converses in the second part of this activity is truly enriching for many students.

For **Triangle Search** to be successful, we have found it helpful for kids to work in pairs and then compare results with at least one other pair. The benefits of cooperation have been very obvious to our students during this activity, since different results were invariably obtained on the first attempt. In fact, this activity helped win over to this approach some students formerly reluctant to work with others. Also, you need to emphasize to your students that they must avoid dragging the figures and to remind them that they can use the **Edit I Undo** feature if they accidentally alter the sketch. After completing the activity, our students enjoy dragging the design into other shapes. Alternatively, you may want to design a more constrained figure for some groups of students.

The activity **The Real Real Number Line** is more challenging than most others in this book. For many middle school classes, it may be appropriate to use it only as a teacher demonstration. For others, we have gone through almost the entire activity with a student sitting at the computer while the teacher verbally led students through the activity. In this case, the focus was on students' gaining Sketchpad skills and on reinforcing the location of commonly encoun-

tered irrational numbers when they did their own follow-up constructions. Pairs work nicely here. With more advanced groups of students, of course, a shorter, less detailed demonstration is needed. Regardless of their level, every group of middle schoolers requires some discussion about radicals and irrational numbers prior to carrying out the activity. The stage for this activity is set with questions such as "What are irrational numbers?" "Where on the number line is $\sqrt{9}$?" and "Between what two whole numbers will you find $\sqrt{18}$?" Regardless of the format in which it is used, we have been pleased with the impact of this activity. It is the first time the real number line truly becomes real for students. Students repeatedly comment, "Now the number line in my head is fuller," or "Constructing my own Sketchpad number line helped me remember what $\sqrt{2}$ is." If your paper supply is generous, it is helpful to have students print an extra copy of their number line showing all hidden features. We often ask students to save a copy of their sketches on a disk so we can check them for verification or construction errors.

Slice It, Dice It can be extended nicely for algebra students. If the drawings are done on a grid, questions and observations about slope are appropriate and interesting.

Kids really get into **PT Problems** as a follow-up to **Exploring the Pythagorean Theorem.** Having students present their problems in class for others to solve is a motivating, effective method of alternative assessment. Again, pairs work well here.

Don't overlook **Pythagoras Plus.** Students of all ages (including most adults) feel like "real mathematicians" as they discover the extension of the Pythagorean theorem on their own. It is a wonderful attribute of Sketchpad that a student who lacks the skill to find the area of regular polygons beyond squares can have the same feeling of accomplishment as others with more experience, since Sketchpad will calculate and display the area for the student. For some students, you may need to provide detailed instructions or a custom tool for the construction of the regular polygons. For others, doing their own constructions is the highlight of the activity.

Before students attempt the project **A Look Inside,** you need to demonstrate the Sketchpad skill of constructing a midpoint of a side and then a new segment for each half. This project is technically more difficult than most projects in this book. It fits nicely into a fractals unit.

If your students explore tessellations with triangles (see number 3 in **More Ideas for Triangles Projects**), we have found that exploring with equilateral triangles first is the most successful route for most middle school students because it is technically so much easier. Of course, you can approach this topic by tessellating first with a scalene triangle. Then the students can drag a vertex and watch the triangles change from scalene to isosceles or equilateral if their Sketchpad proficiency is sufficient.

Prerequisite Mathematical Terms and Concepts

- *vertex, ray, acute angle, right angle, obtuse angle*
- names and rules for types of triangles classified by sides (scalene, isosceles, equilateral) and by angles (acute, obtuse, right)

Recommended Sketchpad Proficiency

- Basic knowledge of the freehand tools.
- Use of the Polygons Quick Reference Guide at the end of this unit is suggested.
- Doing the Points, Lines, and Angles unit prior to this one would be beneficial; otherwise, you might want to use specific sketches from that unit as student questions arise.

Essential Vocabulary

Acute triangle—a triangle with three acute angles

Equilateral triangle—a triangle with all sides congruent

Exterior angle—any angle formed outside a polygon by one side of a polygon and the extension of an adjacent side

Hypotenuse—side opposite the right angle in a right triangle

Interior angle—any angle formed within a polygon by two adjacent sides

Isosceles triangle—a triangle with at least two congruent sides

Leg—one of the sides forming the right angle in a right triangle

Obtuse triangle—a triangle with one obtuse angle

Right triangle—a triangle with one right angle

Scalene triangle—a triangle with no congruent sides

Triangle—a polygon with three sides

Instructions for Teacher Demonstrations

In each unit, we have included sketches and guidelines for demonstrations the teacher can use to introduce the material to the whole class before students attempt the various activities independently. They include the introduction of relevant mathematical vocabulary and concepts as well as appropriate Sketchpad skills. Often there are several activities that you will feel comfortable assigning to your students with very little guidance beforehand. In this unit, for example, the activities **Altitudes** and **Angles** work fine as exploratory introductions to those topics and require very little technical expertise. For **Area,** on the other hand, students should know the formula for finding the area of a triangle. In addition, you might want to demonstrate how to use Sketchpad to display area before assigning the activity. One or more activities in each unit are designed to maximize guided discovery by the students. For these activities, a careful teacher demonstration will focus the students' attention on targeted mathematical concepts and prevent distractions due to lack of Sketchpad proficiency. In this unit, the activities **Exploring Properties of Triangles, Exploring Types of Triangles,** and **Exploring the Pythagorean Theorem** are designed to follow such a demonstration. Instructions are included later in these notes, along with answers for the guided discovery activities, for your convenience. Of course, you may want to use portions or adaptations of the demonstrations before other activities; certainly, you will want to preview activities to be sure they are appropriate for the mathematical and Sketchpad skill levels of your students. The teacher demonstrations will help ensure success with most of the activities in this unit, since the topics related to triangles come early in most middle school geometry curricula, and needed Sketchpad skills, which are introduced in each portion of the demonstration, may be new to many of your students. Each new Sketchpad skill may require several repetitions. We often show several examples and then at the close of each teacher demonstration, have a student sit at the computer while another student gives verbal instructions.

You may find the Polygons Quick Reference Guide at the end of this unit helpful in preparing for the triangles demonstrations.

Exploring Properties of Triangles

"Triangles Demos" 1–4 are pages in the sketch **Triangles Demos.gsp.**

1. Demonstrate the following Sketchpad skills using "Triangles Demo 1":

   • Drag a vertex using the **Selection Arrow** tool ⬧.

   • Move labels using the **Text** tool Ⓐ.

   • Move captions or measures using the **Selection Arrow** tool ⬧.

   • Find the sum of angles using **Calculate** from the Measure menu.

2. Demonstrate the following Sketchpad skills using "Triangles Demo 2":

   • Manipulate segments to given lengths.

   • Make endpoints of segments meet (or not) to form vertices of a triangle.

Exploring Types of Triangles

1. Discuss classifications of triangles by sides and by angles. Go to the page "Triangles Demo 3" and drag to illustrate each of the following:

   • Scalene triangle

   • Isosceles triangle

   • Equilateral triangle

   • Acute triangle

   • Obtuse triangle

   • Right triangle

2. Explain that the triangle in each sketch used by students in **Exploring Types of Triangles** (with the exception of the scalene triangle) will remain that kind of triangle when dragged; in other words, in the isosceles triangle sketch, the triangle will always remain isosceles, and in the equilateral triangle sketch, the triangle will always remain equilateral. For the scalene triangle sketch, emphasize to students that they should observe the measures of the sides to keep the triangle scalene as they drag to answer the questions.

Exploring the Pythagorean Theorem

1. Review angles, if needed. Open a new sketch. Use the **Segment** tool ╱ to construct an angle. Drag to show acute, right, and obtuse angles.

Triangles

2. Review right triangles, including the terms *hypotenuse* and *legs*. Go to the page "Triangles Demo 4" and drag to illustrate each of the following Sketchpad skills:

- Build a table using **Tabulate** from the Graph menu.
- Manipulate segments to given lengths.

Writing Prompts

Ask students to choose a topic below and to write a short paper, including sketches created with Sketchpad.

- All I Know About Triangles
- Triangles Everywhere
- Pythagoras Lives
- Triangles Are Confusing!?

Examples of Student Work

Triangles Project: Pythagoras Plus

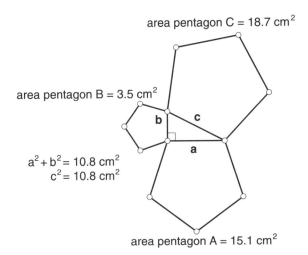

area pentagon C = 18.7 cm^2

area pentagon B = 3.5 cm^2

$a^2 + b^2 = 10.8$ cm^2
$c^2 = 10.8$ cm^2

area pentagon A = 15.1 cm^2

Triangles Project: PT Problems

Slide, Billy Bob, Slide

Billy Bob was at the top of a slide! 125 ft high. His mother was waiting at the bottom of the slide for him. From the bottom of the slide to the bottom of the ladder is 58 ft. How long was Billy Bob's ride down the slide?

By Hee-Young, Katy, and Sarah K.

Billy Bob

slide
slide = 138 pixels

ladder = 125 pixels

ladder

$c^2 = a^2 + b^2$
$c^2 = 125^2 + 58^2$
$c^2 = 15625 + 3364$
$c^2 = 18989$
$\sqrt{18989} = 137.8$ ft

Mom

b
b = 58 pixels

Answers for Exploring Properties of Triangles Activity

Be sure you discuss with students the effects of rounding in this activity.

6. The sum of the angle measures in any triangle is 180°.

7. a. The angle measures are also equal.
   b. The angle measures are not equal.
   c. The lengths of the two sides are also equal.
   d. The lengths of those two sides are not equal.

8. Answers will vary. One acceptable response: The longest side in any triangle is opposite the largest angle, and the shortest side in any triangle is opposite the smallest angle.

11. a. 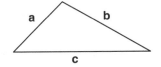   b. impossible   c. impossible

d.

e.

f. impossible

12. Answers will vary. One acceptable response: The sum of the lengths of two sides was less than the length of the third side.

13. Answers will vary. One acceptable response: The sum of the lengths of any two sides of a triangle is always greater than the length of the third side.

Answers for Exploring Types of Triangles Activity

Be sure you discuss with students the effects of rounding in this activity.

2. a. yes   b. yes   c. yes
4. a. yes   b. yes   c. yes
6. a. yes   b. no   c. no
7. a. sometimes   b. sometimes   c. never
    d. never   e. never   f. sometimes
    g. always   h. always

Answers for Exploring the Pythagorean Theorem Activity

Be sure you discuss with students the effects of rounding in this activity.

4. For each right triangle, the sum of a^2 and b^2 is equal to c^2.

6. (Wording may vary.) In a right triangle, the square of the hypotenuse is equal to the sum of the squares of the other two sides.

9. a. no, no, 90°   b. no, no, 90°   c. no, no, 90°
    d. no, no, 90°   e. no, no, 90°   f. no, no, 90°

10. a. yes   b. no   c. yes, yes, no

11. (Wording may vary.) A triangle will be a right triangle only when the square of the hypotenuse is equal to the sum of the squares of the other two sides.

Solution for Triangle Search Activity

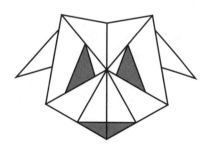

acute triangles <u>11</u>

obtuse triangles <u>9</u>

right triangles <u>4</u>

number of different sizes of triangle <u>13</u>

scalene triangles <u>12</u>

isosceles triangles <u>12</u> (including equilateral triangles)

equilateral triangles <u>2</u>

total number of triangles <u>24</u>

Answers for Triangles Wrap-Up

1. yes

2. no

3. yes

4. b, c, a

5. c, a, b

6. a, b, c

7. c, b, b

8. c, b, a

9. a, b, c

10–15. Drawings will vary. Triangles described in questions 13 and 14 are impossible.

Altitudes

1. Open the sketch **Tri Altitudes.gsp.**

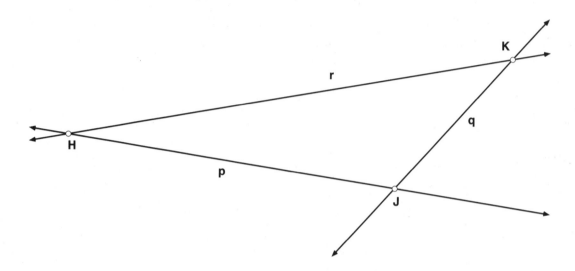

2. Construct a perpendicular line from any vertex of the triangle to the opposite side. Change its color or make it dashed. Construct the point of intersection of the line and the side of the triangle. The segment from the vertex to this point of intersection is called an *altitude* of the triangle.

3. Drag any of the points **H**, **J**, or **K** to make an acute triangle. Describe the placement of the altitude. Write your conjecture. _____

_____

_____

4. Drag any of the points **H**, **J**, or **K** to make a right triangle. Describe the placement of the altitude. Does it matter which angle is the right angle? Write your conjecture.

_____

_____

5. Drag any of the points **H**, **J**, or **K** to make an obtuse triangle. Describe the placement of the altitude. Does it matter which angle is the obtuse angle? Write your conjecture. _____

_____

_____

Area

1. Open the sketch **Tri Area.gsp.** Note that the dashed line is parallel to side **GH.**

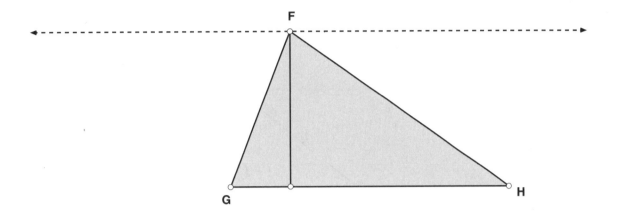

2. Use Sketchpad to determine the area of the triangle in two different ways. Use side **GH** as the base.

3. Now drag vertex **F** or use the Animation button to change the shape of the triangle. Observe the effect on the area. Make conjectures and explain your reasoning.

_____

_____

_____

Test your conjectures by dragging the dashed line or one of the points **G** or **H**. Do your conjectures still hold? Explain. _____

_____

_____

Angles

1. Open a new sketch.

2. Construct a triangle.

3. Extend one side by constructing a ray using two vertices.

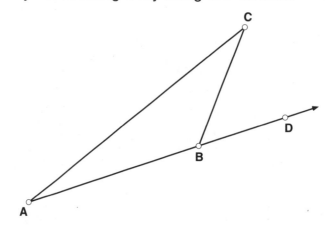

4. Measure each of the interior angles.

5. Go to the Measure menu and choose **Calculate.** Use Sketchpad's calculator to determine the sum of the three interior angles.

6. Drag any vertex of the triangle and observe the measures of the interior angles and their sum.

7. Write any conjectures based on your exploration. _____

    _____

    _____

8. Click somewhere on the ray outside the triangle to construct a point. Measure the exterior angle.

9. Use Sketchpad's calculator to determine the sum of the two interior angles that are not adjacent to the exterior angle (**CAB** and **ACB**).

10. Drag any vertex of the triangle and compare the measure of the exterior angle to the sum of the two remote (nonadjacent) interior angles.

11. Write any conjectures based on your exploration. _____

    _____

    _____

Exploring Properties of Triangles

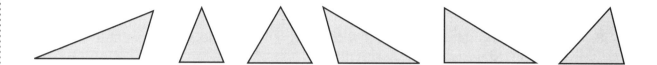

1. Open the sketch **Exploring Triangles.gsp** and go to the page "Exploring Triangles 1."

You will use the Sketchpad calculator to find the sum of the measures of the angles in any triangle.

2. Go to the Measure menu and choose **Calculate.**

3. Click on one of the angle measures that is showing in your sketch.

4. Click on the Plus (**+**) in the New Calculation dialog box and then click on another angle measure showing in your sketch.

5. Click on the Plus (**+**) again and click on the third angle measure. Then click OK.

6. Drag any vertex and observe the sum of the angle measures. What can you conclude about the sum of the measures of the angles of any triangle?

_____

Now you will explore the measures of the angles and the lengths of the sides opposite those angles.

7. Drag any vertex to change the size and shape of your triangle. Observe the measures of the angles and the lengths of the sides. Answer the questions below.

   a. If the lengths of two sides of a triangle are equal, what do you know about the measures of the angles opposite them? _____

   _____

   b. If the lengths of two sides of a triangle are unequal, what do you know about the measures of the angles opposite them?_____

   _____

   c. If the measures of two angles of a triangle are equal, what do you know about the lengths of the sides opposite them?_____

   _____

d. If the measures of two angles of a triangle are unequal, what do you know about the lengths of the sides opposite them? _____

_____

8. Summarize the relationship in any triangle between the measures of the angles and the lengths of the sides opposite them. _____

_____

_____

_____

Now you will explore the relationship among the lengths of the sides of a triangle.

9. Go to the page "Exploring Triangles 2."

10. Drag the endpoints of the parallel segments to adjust the measures of the sides of your figure. Then swing the endpoints of the figure to see whether you can make a triangle. The endpoints must meet to form the vertices of the triangle.

11. Try to construct a triangle using the following lengths for the three sides. For each example, sketch your triangle or write *impossible* in the box.

	Side a	Side b	Side c	Triangle?
a.	2.0 cm	3.0 cm	4.0 cm	
b.	6.0 cm	1.0 cm	4.0 cm	
c.	3.5 cm	2.0 cm	6.0 cm	
d.	3.0 cm	4.0 cm	4.0 cm	
e.	5.0 cm	5.0 cm	6.0 cm	
f.	2.0 cm	7.0 cm	4.0 cm	

12. Why was it impossible to construct a triangle with some of the given lengths?

_____

_____

13. Experiment with other lengths. Write a statement about the relationship among the lengths of the three sides of a triangle. _____

_____

_____

Exploring Types of Triangles

What am I? Scalene? Isosceles? Equilateral? Acute? Right? Obtuse?

Use Sketchpad to explore more types of triangles.

1. Open the sketch **Triangles.gsp** and go to the page "Scalene."

2. The sketch shows you the angle measures and side lengths. As you drag to answer the questions below, make sure you keep the measures of all three sides different so that the triangle remains scalene.

   a. Can you have a scalene triangle that is also an *acute* triangle? _____

   b. Can you have a scalene triangle that is also an *obtuse* triangle? _____

   c. Can you have a scalene triangle that is also a *right* triangle? _____

3. Go to the page "Isosceles Triangle."

4. The sketch shows you the angle measures and side lengths. Drag the figure and answer the following questions.

   a. Can you have an isosceles triangle that is also an *acute* triangle? _____

   b. Can you have an isosceles triangle that is also an *obtuse* triangle? _____

   c. Can you have an isosceles triangle that is also a *right* triangle? _____

5. Go to the page "Equilateral Triangle."

6. The sketch shows you the angle measures and side lengths. Drag the figure and answer the following questions.

   a. Can you have an equilateral triangle that is also an *acute* triangle? _____

   b. Can you have an equilateral triangle that is also an *obtuse* triangle? _____

   c. Can you have an equilateral triangle that is also a *right* triangle? _____

7. Use any of the three sketches (if needed) to tell whether each statement below is true *always, sometimes,* or *never.*

   a. An acute triangle is isosceles. _____

   b. An obtuse triangle is scalene. _____

   c. An obtuse triangle contains a right angle. _____

   d. A triangle contains two obtuse angles. _____

   e. A right triangle is equilateral. _____

   f. An isosceles triangle is equilateral. _____

   g. A right triangle has two acute angles. _____

   h. An equilateral triangle is isosceles. _____

Geometry Activities for Middle School Students with The Geometer's Sketchpad
©2004 Key Curriculum Press

Exploring the Pythagorean Theorem*

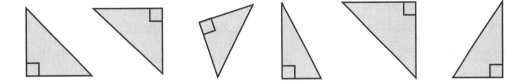

1. Open the sketch **Pythagoras.gsp** and go to the page "Pythagoras 1."

2. Notice the following features of the figure.

   a. Triangle **TRY** is a right triangle.

   b. The figure constructed on each side of △**TRY** is a square.

   c. For each square, the length of each side equals the length of one side of the triangle.

   d. The lengths of the sides of the triangle and squares are shown in the sketch.

   e. The areas of the squares are shown.

3. Using the displayed measures of the areas of the squares, build a table to show the values as you change the triangle.

   a. Click on the displayed measures of a^2, b^2, and c^2.

   b. Go to the Graph menu and choose **Tabulate.**

   c. Drag the resulting table of values to a convenient location in your sketch.

   d. Drag **T** or **Y**.

   e. Double-click on the table to add a new column.

   f. Repeat steps d and e until you have added several columns.

4. Do you see any relationship among the values in your table? If yes, explain.

   Note: Keep in mind that measurements are rounded to the nearest tenth of a square centimeter.

   _____

   _____

   _____

   _____

*There is evidence that special cases of this theorem were known in Babylon (present-day Iran and Iraq) at least 1000 years before Pythagoras lived. There exists what some consider a proof of this theorem by a Chinese mathematician in *Zhoubi suajing,* which may date from before Pythagoras's time. For more details, see Victor J. Katz, *A History of Mathematics* (HarperCollins, 1995).

If no, do the following: Add a^2 and b^2. Notice how the sum compares with c^2. Now state the relationship in the space above.

> *Tip:* To calculate the sum of a^2 and b^2 in your sketch, go to the Measure menu and choose **Calculate.** You can use Sketchpad's calculator to find the sum for you.

5. Drag vertices **T** and **Y** to determine whether this relationship always seems to exist.

6. Explain in your own words what this activity tells you about the relationship among the sides of any right triangle.

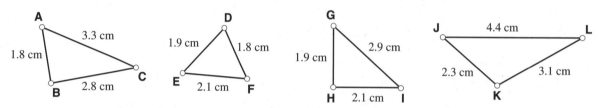

7. Go to the page "Pythagoras 2."

   Notice that the following measures are displayed: the lengths of **a, b,** and **c;** the values of a^2, b^2, and c^2; the measure of ∠**NOW**; and the value of $a^2 + b^2$.

8. Drag the endpoints of the parallel segments on the right side of your sketch to change the lengths of sides **a, b,** and **c** in your sketch. Drag vertices **N** and **W** to change the size of ∠**NOW**.

   Notice that dragging **N** and **W** changes the angle measure of ∠**NOW** and side **c** but not the lengths of **a** and **b**. Also, notice that dragging segments **a** and **b** changes the lengths of **a, b,** and **c** but not the measure of ∠**NOW**.

9. Drag **a** and **b** to the designated lengths, and then drag vertex **N** or **W** to change the measure of ∠**NOW** to answer the questions and complete the table.

	Side a	Side b	Can you drag N and/or W so that ∠NOW is acute and $a^2 + b^2 = c^2$?	Can you drag N and/or W so that ∠NOW is obtuse and $a^2 + b^2 = c^2$?	Drag N and/or W until $a^2 + b^2 = c^2$. What is the measure of ∠NOW when this happens?
a.	3.0 cm	4.0 cm			
b.	1.5 cm	2.0 cm			
c.	0.5 cm	1.2 cm			
d.	6.0 cm	8.0 cm			
e.	3.4 cm	2.4 cm			
f.	3.5 cm	3.5 cm			

10. Use your results from step 9 to answer each question below.

   a. If the sum of the squares of the two short sides ($a^2 + b^2$) equals the square of the longest side (c^2) in a triangle, is it *always* a right triangle? _____

   b. If the sum of the squares of the two short sides ($a^2 + b^2$) does not equal the square of the longest side (c^2), can you ever have a right triangle? _____

   c. Can you have a right triangle with the side lengths shown below? Write yes or no for each.

   20, 21, 29 _____

   8, 15, 17 _____

   8, 10, 13 _____

11. Complete this statement about the relationship of side lengths in right triangles:

   A triangle will be a right triangle only when _____

   _____.

1. Open the sketch **Triangle Search.gsp**.

2. Being careful not to drag any points or change any shapes in any way, work together to complete the activity: Count the total of each kind of triangle found in the figure below. Be sure to include triangles formed by two or more individual shapes. Use Sketchpad tools and the Measure menu to verify lengths of sides and measures of angles when needed.

   Remember: You can measure the length of a side by selecting the side and choosing **Length** from the Measure menu. However, when a segment serves as a side to several triangles, you may need to select the two endpoints of the side of your triangle and choose **Distance** from the Measure menu. Also, do not add two parts of a side to get its length. Instead, always select the endpoints of the side you wish to measure and choose **Distance** from the Measure menu.

3. Put your name(s) on your sketch and print out a copy to hand in.

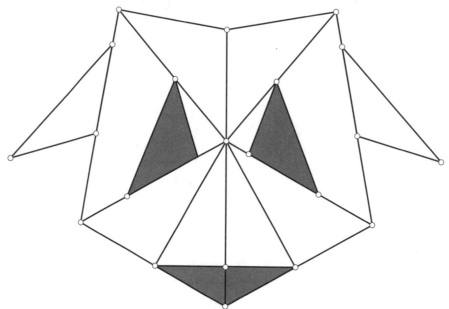

acute triangles _____   scalene triangles _____
obtuse triangles _____   isosceles triangles _____
right triangles _____   equilateral triangles _____
number of different sizes of triangles _____   total number of triangles _____

Geometry Activities for Middle School Students with The Geometer's Sketchpad
©2004 Key Curriculum Press

The Real Real Number Line

In this activity, you will construct a Sketchpad number line that will display some irrational numbers as well as the whole numbers traditionally displayed on a number line.

1. Open a new sketch. Go to the Edit menu and choose **Preferences.** Change the distance unit to inches if needed.

2. Using the **Line** tool 📐, draw a horizontal line in your sketch.

3. Using the **Selection Arrow** tool 🔺, select both points on the line.

4. Go to the Display menu and choose **Hide Points.**

5. Select the line. Go to the Construct menu and choose **Point On Line.**

6. Using the **Text** tool 𝔸, click on the point on your horizontal line to display its label. Double-click on the label and change its name to 0 (to mark it as the zero point on your number line).

7. Using the **Selection Arrow** tool 🔺, select the zero point. Go to the Transform menu and choose **Translate.** Enter the values in the dialog box shown at right and click Translate.

Translate Dialog Box (Macintosh)

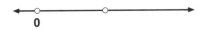

8. Continue translating each new point until you have a number line at least 5 inches long. Label the points as they appear below.

9. Select the horizontal line and the zero point on that line. Go to the Construct menu and choose **Perpendicular Line.**

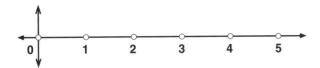

10. Select the zero point and translate it vertically 1 inch.

11. Select the point 0, the point 1, and the translated point and construct segments between them to create a right triangle. (You may want to hide the vertical perpendicular line before you do this.)

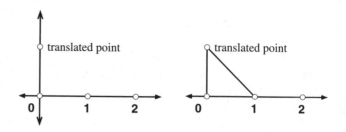

12. Select the hypotenuse and the zero point. Go to the Construct menu and choose **Circle By Center+Radius.**

13. Click on the point of intersection of the circle and the number line to construct the point √2 on your number line.

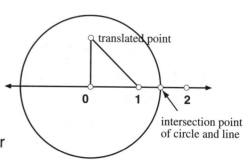

Hide your circle and the hypotenuse. Label this point.

Note: On a Macintosh, type Option+V to display √. With Windows, use the Symbol font, then hold down the Alt key while you type 0214 on the number keypad.

14. Construct a segment between the translated point and the point √2. This construction yields a 1-√2-√3 right triangle.

15. Select the hypotenuse and the zero point. Go to the Construct menu and chose **Circle By Center+Radius.**

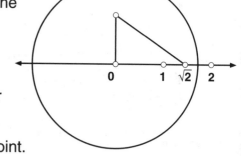

16. Click on the point of intersection of the circle and the number line to construct the point √3 on your number line.

17. Hide your circle and the hypotenuse. Label this point.

18. Repeat the above process to construct the points √5, √6, and √7 on your number line, as shown below. Be sure to hide objects.

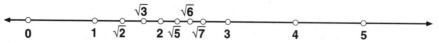

19. Print out a copy of your sketch to hand in.

20. Using your pencil, place labeled points on the printed copy of your number line to approximate the numbers √10, 2.5, √15, 3.75, √16, √18, and √24.

Slice It, Dice It

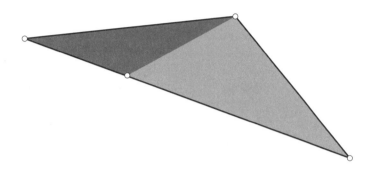

1. Use Sketchpad to construct a triangle. Divide the triangle into exactly two smaller triangles.

2. Is it possible for these two smaller triangles to have the same area? Make a conjecture. (It may be helpful to choose **Preferences** from the Display menu and set the distance unit to **tenths.**) _____

   _____

   _____

   _____

3. Does your conjecture depend on a particular type of original triangle? Is there just one such pair of triangles? Will the two smaller triangles ever be congruent? Use sketches to help you. Explain your reasoning. _____

   _____

   _____

   _____

PT Problems

Create a word problem of your own that can be solved by using the Pythagorean Theorem. Put the problem, a drawing, and the solution in a sketch. Put your name on the sketch and print out a copy to hand in.

Student Example:

Emily is riding her bicycle on straight roads 12 miles due south, then 5 miles due east. If Katy starts at the same place and bikes along a straight diagonal road that ends where Emily does, how far must Katy bike?

Example Solution:

In the diagram, **a** = 12 miles, **b** = 5 miles, and the triangle is a right triangle. You must find **c**.

$$a^2 + b^2 = c^2$$
$$5^2 + 12^2 = c^2$$
$$25 + 144 = c^2$$
$$169 = c^2$$
$$13 = c$$

Katy must bike 13 miles.

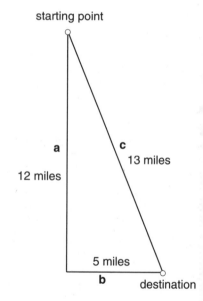

starting point

a

12 miles

c
13 miles

5 miles

b

destination

Pythagoras Plus

Use Sketchpad to explore further with the Pythagorean Theorem. Remember how we used squares on the sides of a right triangle to show the Pythagorean Theorem? Recall that in a right triangle the square of the hypotenuse is equal to the sum of the squares of the other two sides. Do you think this relationship will hold for polygons besides squares? Test the idea.

1. Open a new sketch and construct a right triangle. Next, construct a regular polygon (a polygon with all sides congruent and all angles congruent) of some kind so that the hypotenuse is one side of the polygon. Construct the same kind of regular polygon on each leg of your triangle, using the leg as one side of your polygon. Construct the polygon interiors.

2. Use the Measure menu and the Sketchpad calculator to find and display the area of your three polygons. Show whether the area of the figure constructed on side **a** plus the area of the figure constructed on side **b** equals the area of the figure constructed on hypotenuse **c** in your sketch. Print out a copy with all measures and your conclusions displayed. Turn it in to your teacher.

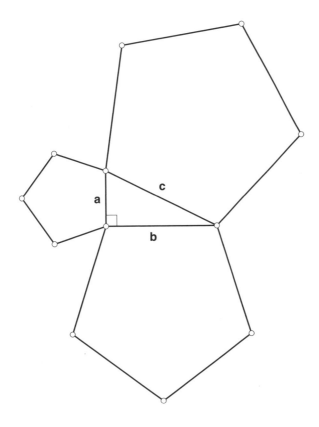

A Look Inside

Use Sketchpad to investigate the effects of subdividing triangles.

1. Construct a triangle and use **Calculate** from the
   Measure menu to find its perimeter. Call this Stage 0
   because this is the figure before any changes are
   made.

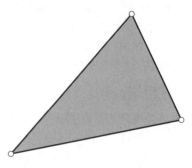

2. For Stage 1, find the midpoint of each side of your
   triangle and construct four smaller congruent
   triangles. Find the sum of the perimeters of the three
   corner triangles.

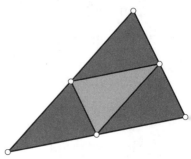

3. For Stage 2, find the midpoint of each side of your
   corner triangles and construct four smaller congruent
   triangles inside each. Find the sum of the perimeters
   of the nine corner triangles within the original corner
   triangles.

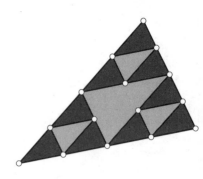

4. Compare the total perimeters for each stage and look for patterns. Write any
   conjectures and explain your reasoning. _____

   _____

   _____

   _____

   Test your conjectures by dragging any vertex of the original triangle. You can also
   create more stages to test your conjectures.

5. Investigate *total area* using the same stages.

1. Use Sketchpad to construct an equilateral triangle. Place a point anywhere inside the triangle and construct a segment perpendicular to each side of the triangle from that point. Find the sum of the three segments. Drag a vertex of the triangle or your interior point. Make any conjectures you can.

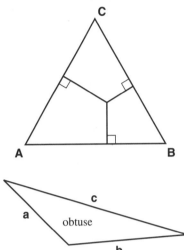

2. The Pythagorean theorem states that for every right triangle, the square of the longest side equals the sum of the squares of the other two sides. Use Sketchpad to explore this kind of comparison in acute triangles. How does the square of the longest side compare to the sum of the squares of the other two sides? How do these compare in obtuse triangles?

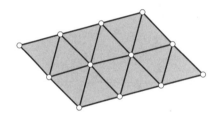

3. Use Sketchpad to explore tessellations with triangles. Try to tessellate the plane with each type of triangle (equilateral, isosceles, scalene, right, acute, and obtuse). What conjectures can you make?

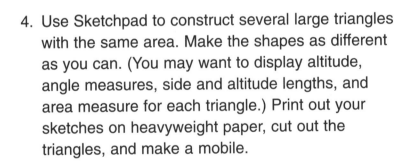

4. Use Sketchpad to construct several large triangles with the same area. Make the shapes as different as you can. (You may want to display altitude, angle measures, side and altitude lengths, and area measure for each triangle.) Print out your sketches on heavyweight paper, cut out the triangles, and make a mobile.

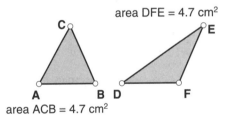

area DFE = 4.7 cm²

area ACB = 4.7 cm²

5. Use Sketchpad to construct several large triangles. Create as many different shapes as you can. Label each triangle according to its sides and according to its angles. Print out your sketches, cut out the triangles, and make a mobile.

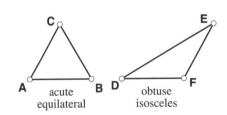

acute
equilateral

obtuse
isosceles

For each set of lengths in questions 1–3, tell whether it is possible to draw a triangle with sides of those measures. Write yes or no.

1. 6 cm, 8 cm, 10 cm

_____

2. 3.5 in., 4.5 in., 8 in.

_____

3. $2\frac{3}{4}$ in., $2\frac{1}{4}$ in., 1 in.

_____

For each triangle in questions 4–6, use the labels given to list the sides in order from shortest to longest.

4. _____

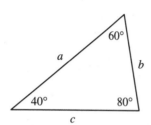

5. _____

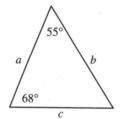

6. _____

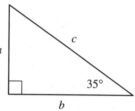

For each triangle in questions 7–9, use the labels given to list the angles in order from smallest to largest.

7. _____

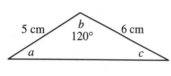

8. _____

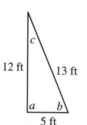

9. _____

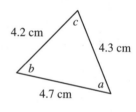

Draw an example of each type of triangle in questions 10–15. If it cannot be done, write *impossible* in the space.

10. acute isosceles triangle

11. obtuse scalene triangle

12. right isosceles triangle

13. obtuse equilateral triangle

14. right equilateral triangle

15. acute scalene triangle

To measure the length of a line segment (use the **Selection Arrow** tool ⬚)

1. Click on the segment.

2. Go to the Measure menu and choose **Length.**

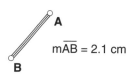

$m\overline{AB} = 2.1$ cm

To measure the distance between two points (use the **Selection Arrow** tool ⬚)

1. Click on one of the points and then on the other.

2. Go to the Measure menu and choose **Distance.**

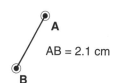

$AB = 2.1$ cm

To measure an angle (use the **Selection Arrow** tool ⬚)

1. Click on three points you could use to name the angle, with the vertex your middle selection.

2. Go to the Measure menu and select **Angle.**

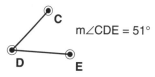

$m\angle CDE = 51°$

To sum measures (use the **Selection Arrow** tool ⬚)

1. Go to the Measure menu and choose **Calculate.**

2. Click on one of the measures that is showing in your sketch.

3. Click on Plus (+) in the New Calculation dialog box and then click on another measure showing in your sketch.

4. Repeat until all the measures you wish to sum appear, then click OK.

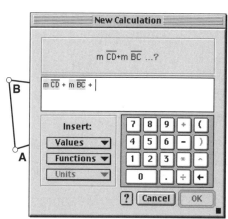

New Calculation Dialog Box (Macintosh)

To display a label and move it (use the **Text** tool $\boxed{A}$)

1. Click on the object. For a segment, click on the segment itself, not on the endpoints.

2. To move the label, click on the label and drag it to any location close to the object.

To make a table (use the **Selection Arrow** tool $\boxed{\nwarrow}$)

1. Click on the measures you wish to show in your table.

2. Go to the Graph menu and choose **Tabulate.**

3. Drag the table of values to a convenient place in your sketch.

4. Drag your object to change its measurements.

5. Double-click on your table to add a new row of data. Repeat steps 4 and 5 to add new values.

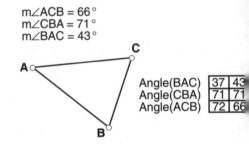

m∠ACB = 66°
m∠CBA = 71°
m∠BAC = 43°

	37	43
Angle(BAC)	37	43
Angle(CBA)	71	71
Angle(ACB)	72	66

To construct a polygon interior (use the **Selection Arrow** tool $\boxed{\nwarrow}$)

1. Click on the vertices of the polygon in order, either clockwise or counterclockwise.

2. Go to the Construct menu and choose **Pentagon Interior** or another appropriate command.

To measure perimeter or area of a polygon (use the **Selection Arrow** tool $\boxed{\nwarrow}$)

1. Construct the polygon interior, if you haven't done so already.

2. Click on the polygon interior.

3. Go to the Measure menu and choose **Perimeter** or **Area.**

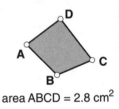

area ABCD = 2.8 cm²

To write your name(s) on a sketch and then print (use the **Text** tool $\boxed{A}$)

1. Double-click in a blank area in your sketch to create a text box.

2. Type your name(s) in this box.

3. Go to the File menu and choose **Print.**

Becky and David

QUADRILATERALS

Commentary

Teaching quadrilaterals had always been difficult for us. Year after year, students took notes faithfully, did well on a quiz when asked to list the characteristics of each type of quadrilateral, "played" diligently with shapers (cardboard strips used to help clarify characteristics), and then (ugh!) did poorly on the unit test.

With The Geometer's Sketchpad, the experience was quite different. After a day of introductory work in the classroom demonstrating each type of quadrilateral with Sketchpad and an overhead projector, we went to the computer lab, where students completed the activity **Exploring Quadrilaterals,** working in pairs. There we discovered the importance of demonstrating how to test a pair of sides or angles for congruence—because it had been a while since we had worked in the lab, most of the kids had forgotten how to do that with Sketchpad.

If your students are at a level where they would benefit from exploring the concept of simple closed figures, the activity **Simple Closed Figures** is an appropriate way to introduce them to the dynamic figures that are created using Sketchpad.

In **Exploring Quadrilaterals,** students should discover the properties of various types of quadrilaterals. They make these discoveries by playing with sketches that are constrained to remain a certain shape. For example, the parallelogram will remain a parallelogram no matter how the students drag its vertices. When a figure such as the parallelogram can be made into a square by dragging, it is easy for most students to conclude that a parallelogram is sometimes a square. By measuring the sides and angles, some kids discover that this happens whenever a pair of adjacent sides is congruent and forms a right angle. While the kids worked, we overheard conversations between and among pairs: "Do we need to measure all the sides of the rhombus? I can tell they're all the same"; "Hey, did you

guys get the trapezoid to turn into anything?"; and "If we got the rectangle to be a square, does that mean a rectangle is always a square or that a square is always a rectangle?" It seemed as if most of the kids were really grasping the properties of each type of quadrilateral and the relationships between the types.

As we went over the activity in class the next day, we were excited to see how clearly the kids seemed to understand the material. A few were shaky on the *sometimes/always/never* questions, but the problem seemed to lie with the format of the questions rather than with their understanding of the properties. We still believe it is important to use this format because of the extra thinking it requires. Students get better at it with practice.

Properties of Quadrilaterals is included as an open-ended alternative to **Exploring Quadrilaterals.** It can be used as a follow-up or an assessment instrument as well.

Diagonals in Quadrilaterals is appropriate only for students who can clearly differentiate among the types of quadrilaterals. Before starting it, we found it very important to go over Sketchpad skills such as constructing the point of intersection for the diagonals and then a new segment for each part. You may want to point out to students that the measure of the length of a segment is the same as the distance between its two endpoints. Because measuring the distance between two points is, in this situation, a simpler maneuver with Sketchpad, you may want to encourage your students to use this method. During this activity, students test the diagonals of several kinds of quadrilaterals to determine whether the diagonals are always congruent, perpendicular, and/or bisectors of each other. Some students need to be prodded to have Sketchpad actually measure angles and segments; they often want to "eyeball" the sketch and guess at the answers. Student comments during the activity made it clear that manipulating the figures in the sketches enabled many of them to see some of the properties clearly for the first time. Back in the classroom, our impressions of their overall understanding were verified when their performance on the unit test was the best ever.

We found **Diagonals Inside and Out** to be especially effective when used in response to questions raised by students about convex versus concave polygons. (Of course, as all middle school teachers know, cleverly guided dialogue by you can often provoke such questions!) Similarly, **Midpoint Quadrilaterals** is most meaningful as a search for answers to "what if" questions: "What happens if you connect the midpoints of the sides of a quadrilateral to construct another quadrilateral inside the original figure?"

Dog Pens lends itself to a cooperative-learning format. Middle school kids enjoy creating a Sketchpad illustration to show their solution.

Quadrilateral Puzzle is harder than it first appears. Students should have done some constructions before being assigned this activity. Doing **Constructing a Rhombus** and/or **Constructing a Parallelogram** (see Unit 7, Constructions) is desirable. If students have made custom tools for constructing quadrilaterals, these would also be appropriate here. Because it is easy to overlook some quadrilaterals when making a key, we found that requiring checks by other students *before* the puzzle is handed in helped reduce student errors.

Prerequisite Mathematical Terms and Concepts

- *polygon, quadrilateral, opposite sides, opposite angles, consecutive sides, consecutive angles, parallel, perpendicular*
- congruent sides, congruent angles

Recommended Sketchpad Proficiency

- Basic knowledge of the freehand tools.
- Use of the Polygons Quick Reference Guide (in the Triangles unit) is suggested.

Essential Vocabulary

Bisect—to divide into two congruent parts (for example, if a point divides a segment into two congruent parts, it bisects the segment; if a ray divides an angle into two congruent angles, it bisects the angle)

Concave polygon—a polygon containing at least one interior angle with measure greater than 180°

Convex polygon—a polygon in which the measure of each interior angle is less than 180°

Diagonal—a segment connecting any two nonconsecutive vertices of a polygon

Intersection point—any point that two geometric shapes have in common

Parallelogram—a quadrilateral with two pairs of parallel sides

Polygon—a simple closed figure in a plane, with segments as sides

Quadrilateral—a polygon with four sides

Rectangle—an equiangular parallelogram

Rhombus—an equilateral parallelogram

Square—an equilateral rectangle

Trapezoid—a quadrilateral with exactly one pair of parallel sides

Instructions for Teacher Demonstrations

In each unit, we have included sketches and guidelines for demonstrations the teacher can use to introduce the material to the whole class before students attempt the various activities independently. They include the introduction of

relevant mathematical vocabulary and concepts as well as appropriate Sketchpad skills. Often there are one or several activities that you will feel comfortable assigning to your students with very little guidance beforehand. In this unit, for example, **Simple Closed Figures** works fine as an exploratory introduction to quadrilaterals and requires very little technical expertise. On the other hand, one or more activities in each unit are designed to maximize guided discovery by the students. For these activities, a careful teacher demonstration will focus the students' attention on targeted mathematical concepts and prevent distractions due to lack of Sketchpad proficiency. In this unit, **Exploring Quadrilaterals** is designed to follow such a demonstration; the instructions are included later in these notes. Of course, you may want to use portions or adaptations of the demonstration before other activities; certainly you will want to preview activities to be sure they are appropriate for the mathematical and Sketchpad skill levels of your students.

You may find the Polygons Quick Reference Guide (at the end of the Triangles unit) helpful in preparing for the quadrilaterals demonstrations.

Exploring Quadrilaterals

1. Discuss quadrilaterals. Open a new sketch, draw a general quadrilateral, and demonstrate the following Sketchpad skills:

   • Set preferences.

     a. Choose **Preferences** from the Display menu.

     b. Select the following settings:

        Distance unit: **cm**

        Angle unit: **degrees**

        Precision: **hundredths**

        Precision: **units**

   • Use the **Text** tool $\boxed{A}$ to change the name for a measure (a name often needs shortening).

2. Explain that the figure in each student sketch will remain that kind of quadrilateral when it is dragged. (We suggest opening the sketch **Quads.gsp** and going to the page "Rhombus." Drag the rhombus to show that it can become a square. Point out that the figure is still a rhombus.)

3. Using a general quadrilateral sketch, demonstrate and discuss the following Sketchpad skills:

   • Test sides and angles for congruence.

   • Find the sum of the angle measures in a quadrilateral using **Calculate** from the Measure menu.

   • Drag a figure to determine relationships ranging from "no relationship" to "all x are always congruent."

   • Drag a figure to test whether it can become another kind of quadrilateral (for example, drag a rectangle to become a square).

   • Drag a figure to determine *sometimes/ always/never* for statements in the form "A type c quadrilateral is *sometimes/ always/never* a type d quadrilateral." Solicit student suggestions for possible statements.

4. Discuss *diagonals, intersection point, bisect.* Demonstrate the following Sketchpad skills using a general quadrilateral sketch:

   • Construct the diagonals of a quadrilateral.

   • Construct the intersection point of diagonals.

   • Measure the length of part or all of a diagonal.

   • Measure angles formed at the intersection point of diagonals.

   • Determine whether two diagonals are perpendicular.

5. Using the various types of quadrilateral sketches in the **Quads.gsp** sketch, discuss dragging.

   - Test diagonals for a particular kind of quadrilateral from the sketch.

   - Determine whether a statement is *always* true for a particular kind of quadrilateral. Solicit student suggestions for possible statements.

Note to teacher: **Constructing a Rhombus** and **Constructing a Parallelogram** (in Unit 7, Constructions) fit nicely with this unit.

Writing Prompts

Ask students to choose a topic below and write a short paper, including sketches created with Sketchpad.

- Introducing the Quadrilateral Family
- A Day in the Life of Quadra Lateral
- Diagonals in Quadrilaterals
- Questions I Have About Quadrilaterals

Example of Student Work

Quadrilateral Puzzle

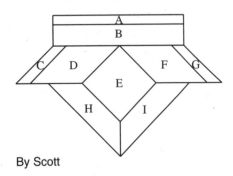

By Scott

Key

Trapezoids (2)	H, I	2 pts.
Squares (1)	E	4 pts.
Rectangles (3)	A, B, A + B	9 pts.
Rhombuses (2)	D, F	6 pts.
Parallelograms (4)	C, G, C + D, F + G	8 pts.
	Total points:	29

Answers for Exploring Quadrilaterals Activity

2. a. all equal   b. all equal   c. always
   d. always   e. always

4. a. all equal   b. Two pairs of opposite angles have equal measures.
   c. always   d. always   e. always
   f. always   g. sometimes   h. always

6. a. Two pairs of opposite sides have equal lengths.   b. all equal
   c. always   d. always   e. always
   f. sometimes   g. always   h. sometimes

8. a. Two pairs of opposite sides have equal lengths.
   b. Two pairs of opposite angles have equal measures.
   c. always   d. always   e. always
   f. sometimes   g. always   h. always

10. a. no relationship   b. no relationship   c. yes
    d. yes   e. no   f. always
    g. never
12. a. no   b. no   c. four-sided
                                                       polygon

Solution for Dog Pens Activity

Diagram in sketch Dog Pens

Solution

Answers for Quadrilaterals Wrap-Up

1. a, c, d, e, g, h   2. a, c, e, h   3. b, f
   parallelogram   rectangle   trapezoid
4. a, h   5. a, g, h   6. a, h
   square   rhombus   square

For questions 7 and 8, answers will vary.

Simple Closed Figures

A *polygon* is a simple closed figure in a plane with segments as sides.

A *quadrilateral* is a polygon with exactly four sides.

Use Sketchpad to explore quadrilaterals as simple closed figures.

1. Open the sketch **Quads Intro.gsp**.

2. A point can move around a *simple closed figure* in a plane tracing a complete path that doesn't cross itself. Animate **Traveller** and observe the path traced on quadrilateral **ABCD**. Is the quadrilateral a simple closed figure? Explain.

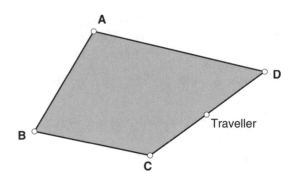

_____

_____

_____

3. Drag any vertex of quadrilateral **ABCD** until it is concave (i.e., until one of the interior angles is greater than 180°). Animate **Traveller** and observe the path traced. Is the figure a simple closed figure? Explain. Is the figure still a quadrilateral? Explain.

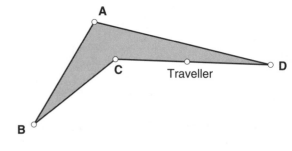

_____

_____

_____

4. Drag any vertex of quadrilateral **ABCD** until two sides cross. Animate **Traveller** and observe the path traced. Is the figure a simple closed figure? Explain. Is the figure still a quadrilateral? Explain.

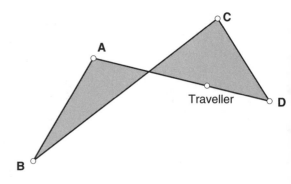

_____

_____

_____

Exploring Quadrilaterals

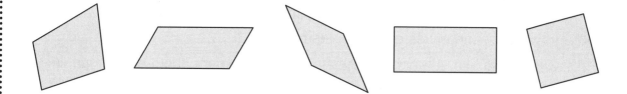

Use Sketchpad to explore some properties of quadrilaterals.

1. Open the sketch **Quads.gsp** and go to the page "Square."

2. Follow the instructions in the sketch. As you drag the figure, answer the following questions.

   a. How are the lengths of the sides related? _____

   b. How are the measures of the angles related? _____

   Answer *sometimes, always,* or *never* for each statement about any square.

   c. A pair of opposite sides are parallel. _____

   d. Both pairs of opposite sides are parallel. _____

   e. All angles are right angles. _____

3. Go to the page "Rhombus."

4. Follow the instructions in the sketch. As you drag the figure, answer the following questions.

   a. How are the lengths of the sides related? _____

   b. How are the measures of the angles related? _____

   Answer *sometimes, always,* or *never* for each statement about any rhombus.

   c. A pair of opposite sides are parallel. _____

   d. Both pairs of opposite sides are parallel. _____

   e. A pair of opposite angles are congruent. _____

   f. Both pairs of opposite angles are congruent. _____

   g. A rhombus is a square. _____

   h. A square is a rhombus. _____

5. Go to the page "Rectangle."

6. Follow the instructions in the sketch. As you drag the figure, answer the following questions.

   a. How are the lengths of the sides related? _____

   b. How are the measures of the angles related? _____

   Answer *sometimes, always,* or *never* for each statement about any rectangle.

   c. A pair of opposite sides are parallel. _____

   d. Both pairs of opposite sides are parallel. _____

   e. All angles are right angles. _____

   f. A rectangle is a square. _____

   g. A square is a rectangle. _____

   h. A rhombus is a rectangle. _____

7. Go to the page "Parallelogram."

8. Follow the instructions in the sketch. As you drag the figure, answer the following questions.

   a. How are the lengths of the sides related? _____

   b. How are the measures of the angles related? _____

   Answer *sometimes, always,* or *never* for each statement about any parallelogram.

   c. A pair of opposite sides are parallel. _____

   d. Both pairs of opposite sides are parallel. _____

   e. A pair of opposite angles are congruent. _____

   f. A parallelogram is a rectangle. _____

   g. A rhombus is a parallelogram. _____

   h. A square is a parallelogram. _____

9. Go to the page "Trapezoid."

10. Follow the instructions in the sketch. As you drag the figure, answer the following questions.

    a. How are the lengths of the sides related? _____

    b. How are the measures of the angles related? _____

    c. Can you drag the trapezoid so that one pair of opposite sides is congruent?

    _____

    d. If the answer to question 10c is yes, are two angles formed in the trapezoid congruent? _____

e. Can you drag the figure so that the trapezoid becomes a parallelogram?

_____

Answer *sometimes, always,* or *never* for each statement about any trapezoid.

   f. One pair of opposite sides is parallel. _____

   g. Both pairs of opposite sides are parallel. _____

11. Go to the page "Quadrilateral."

12. Follow the instructions in the sketch. As you drag the figure, answer the following questions.

   a. Are any side lengths always equal? _____

   b. Are any angle measures always equal? _____

   c. What characteristic(s) apply to *all* quadrilaterals? _____

_____

_____

Properties of Quadrilaterals

| Queenie Quadrilateral | Penelope Parallelogram | Sarah Square | Raphael Rhombus | Ronnie Rectangle | Timmy Trapezoid |

Open the sketch **Quads.gsp**. You will use these pages:

> "Quadrilateral"
> "Parallelogram"
> "Rectangle"
> "Rhombus"
> "Square"
> "Trapezoid"

1. List all the characteristics you can for each type of quadrilateral. Organize your information into a chart or table. Your table might be similar to the one shown here.

Type of Quadrilateral	Characteristics
Quadrilateral	
Parallelogram	
Rectangle	
Rhombus	
Square	
Trapezoid	

Geometry Activities for Middle School Students with The Geometer's Sketchpa
©2004 by Key Curriculum Pre

2. Write the simplest *complete* definition you can for each type of quadrilateral. You may find more than one definition for some types.

Type of Quadrilateral	Definition
Quadrilateral	
Parallelogram	
Rectangle	
Rhombus	
Square	
Trapezoid	

Diagonals in Quadrilaterals

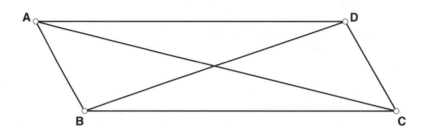

Use Sketchpad to explore the diagonals in several kinds of parallelograms.

1. Open the sketch **Quads.gsp** and go to the page "Parallelogram."

2. Construct the diagonals of the parallelogram.

3. Construct the intersection point of the two diagonals.

4. Measure the length of each diagonal.

5. Drag the parallelogram and then answer the following questions.

   a. Are the lengths of the diagonals in a parallelogram always related in the same way? _____

   b. How are the angles formed by the intersection of the diagonals in a parallelogram related? _____

   _____

   c. List any types of parallelograms in which the diagonals are always congruent.

   _____

   d. List any parallelograms in which all four angles formed by the intersection of the diagonals are congruent.

   _____

   e. List any parallelograms in which the diagonals are always perpendicular.

   _____

   f. List any parallelograms in which the diagonals are always congruent and perpendicular.

   _____

   g. Measure the two parts of each diagonal (remember that the measure of the length of a segment is the same as the distance between its two endpoints). List any parallelograms in which the diagonals always bisect each other.

   _____

6. Drag the parallelogram (if needed) to complete the chart below. Write yes or no in each box.

	Diagonals always congruent?	Diagonals always bisect each other?	Diagonals always perpendicular?
Parallelogram			
Rectangle			
Rhombus			
Square			

Extension: Go to the page "Trapezoid." Construct the diagonals. Drag to explore. Write *sometimes, always,* or *never* for each statement below.

1. The diagonals of a trapezoid are congruent. _____

2. The diagonals of a trapezoid bisect each other. _____

3. The diagonals of a trapezoid are perpendicular. _____

Diagonals Inside and Out

1. Open the sketch **Quads & Diagonals.gsp**.

2. Drag any vertex of quadrilateral **ABCD**, being careful to keep the figure convex (that is, a polygon in which all interior angles are less than 180°). Watch the diagonals as you drag the vertex. Describe the locations of the diagonals with respect to the interior and exterior of the quadrilateral.

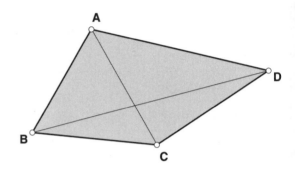

_____

_____

3. Drag any vertex of quadrilateral **ABCD** until it is concave (that is, a polygon in which one of the interior angles is greater than 180°). Describe the locations of the diagonals with respect to the interior and exterior of the quadrilateral.

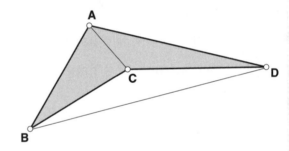

_____

_____

4. Drag any vertex of quadrilateral **ABCD** until two sides cross. Is the figure still a quadrilateral? Explain. Describe the locations of the diagonals with respect to the interior and exterior of the quadrilateral.

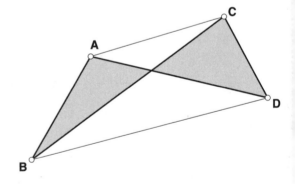

_____

_____

5. Summarize the locations of the two diagonals of figure **ABCD** when it is convex, concave, and not a simple closed figure.

_____

_____

Midpoint Quadrilaterals

1. Construct a quadrilateral. Construct the midpoints of the sides and connect them to construct another quadrilateral inside your original one. We will call the inside figure the *midpoint quadrilateral.*

2. Drag any vertex of the original quadrilateral and compare the area of your midpoint quadrilateral to the area of your original quadrilateral.

3. Make conjectures based on your findings.

_____

_____

_____

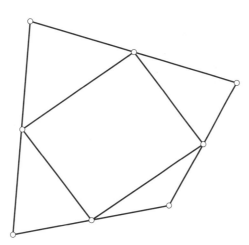

4. What is the shape of the midpoint quadrilateral? Write any conjectures and explain your reasoning.

_____

_____

_____

_____

5. Repeat steps 1–4 for triangles. Write your conjectures about midpoint triangles.

_____

_____

_____

Dog Pens

1. Open the sketch **Dog Pens.gsp.**

2. Working in a group, create a sketch in Sketchpad that solves the problem below.

3. Put your names on your sketch and print out a copy to hand in.

Mr. K. Nine has a square lot for his dogs. He wants to place the dogs as shown below, and he wants a separate pen for each animal. He calls a fencing company and asks them to build two new *square* fences on the lot so that no two dogs share the same pen. Create a sketch for the fencing company to use as a plan.

Quadrilateral Puzzle

1. Working with a partner, create an attractive design in which each individual polygon in your design is a quadrilateral. Check your angle measures and side lengths to be sure you include at least one of each kind of quadrilateral: parallelogram, rhombus, square, rectangle, and trapezoid. If a figure needs parallel or perpendicular sides, be sure to use the Construct menu.

    Remember: Simple is elegant.

2. Now for the hard part: Your design must have a value of less than 50 points, with the value of your design determined as shown below. Give only one value to each shape (the highest number of points possible). For example, don't count a square as both a square and a rectangle. Count it only as a square, since a square is worth more points than a rectangle. *Be sure to include shapes formed by two or more of your individual quadrilaterals when you compute the value!*

    Use the following point values:
    each trapezoid = 1 point
    each parallelogram = 2 points
    each rhombus or rectangle = 3 points
    each square = 4 points

3. Include a key for the value of your design. The key should include the total number and value of *each kind* of quadrilateral as well as the overall value. Check your key by letting other students try your puzzle. (See the example below.)

Bonus: You may earn bonus points if you can create a design worth between 25 and 30 points.

Example:

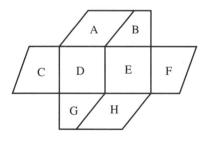

Key

Trapezoids (10)	B, C, F, G, A + B, G + H, C + D, C + D + E, E + F, D + E + F	10 pts.
Squares (2)	D, E	8 pts.
Rectangles (1)	D + E	3 pts.
Rhombuses (2)	A, H	6 pts.
Parallelograms (1)	C + D + E + F	2 pts.
	Total points:	29

1. Use Sketchpad to explore concave quadrilaterals. For example, create sketches to help you explore the sum of the interior or exterior angles in concave quadrilaterals.

    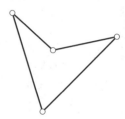

    Note: Sketchpad only displays angle measures less than 180°. When an interior in a concave quadrilateral measures greater than 180°, you will have to use the measure Sketchpad displays to calculate the true angle measure. For angles greater than 180°, the true angle measure is 360° minus the displayed angle measure.

2. Use Sketchpad to explore symmetry in quadrilaterals. Create sketches to demonstrate whether each type of quadrilateral *sometimes, always,* or *never* has reflection or rotation symmetry.

3. Construct a particular type of quadrilateral by focusing on its properties. First, choose one or more properties you feel might be sufficient to define the figure. Then construct the figure using Sketchpad, making sure the figure has the property or properties. Finally, test your figure by dragging to see whether it will always remain that type of quadrilateral. If it does appear to remain that type of quadrilateral, then list the property or properties used to construct it. Repeat for other types of quadrilaterals.

    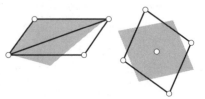

    $m\overline{FG} = 0.7$ inches
    $m\overline{DE} = 0.7$ inches

    Properties: A pair of opposite sides are congruent and parallel.

4. Construct a quadrilateral starting with a pair of diagonals that are related in some way. For example, construct a pair of congruent and perpendicular segments. Then construct the quadrilateral that has these segments as diagonals. Or start with diagonals that are perpendicular but not congruent. Use Sketchpad to create sketches to help you determine how to construct each type of quadrilateral from its diagonals.

    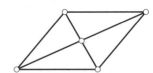

For questions 1–6, read each set of properties and list the letter for each quadrilateral above that has all those properties. Then give the name of that kind of quadrilateral.

1. Two pairs of parallel sides
   Opposite angles congruent
   Opposite sides congruent
   Figures: _____
   Name of quadrilateral: _____

2. Adjacent sides perpendicular
   Opposite sides parallel
   Figures: _____
   Name of quadrilateral: _____

3. Exactly one pair of parallel sides
   Figures: _____
   Name of quadrilateral: _____

4. All sides congruent
   All angles congruent
   Figures: _____
   Name of quadrilateral: _____

5. Opposite angles congruent
   All sides congruent
   Figures: _____
   Name of quadrilateral: _____

6. Diagonals perpendicular
   Diagonals congruent
   Figures: _____
   Name of quadrilateral: _____

For questions 7 and 8, choose any property a quadrilateral may have. List the letters of the quadrilaterals above that have that property and draw another quadrilateral with that same property.

Example: Property: All sides congruent   Drawing
              Figures: a, g, h

7.   Property: _____
      Figures: _____
      Drawing

8.   Property: _____
      Figures: _____
      Drawing

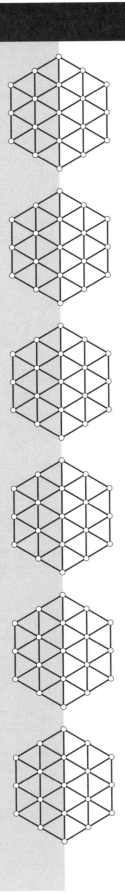

SYMMETRY

ommentary

)ne of the rewards of including a symmetry
nit in the middle school mathematics curricu-
um is that the students are usually unfamiliar
vith the concepts, so they are fresh and eager
> learn. Of course, this unfamiliarity also
neans we have to proceed slowly as we intro-
uce vocabulary and mathematical ideas to our
tudents for the first time.

Mirrors and Reflection is a simple explor-
tory introduction to reflections. Our students
njoy dragging vertices of the pre-image or
mage or the mirror to observe the effects.

Our kids truly seem to enjoy **Reflection and
Rotation Symmetry,** and most are surprised at the
esults for at least one of their figures. Many
otherwise savvy kids will declare confidently
hat a regular pentagon has one line of symme-
ry. Their mouths literally drop open when they
ind they were mistaken. Lots of furrowed brows
urn into "ahas" and smiles by the end of class.

The activities **Diagonals in Parallelograms,
Midsegments in Parallelograms,** and **Rotation
Symmetry in Parallelograms** are great examples
of the adage "Seeing is believing." Kids (and
ometimes teachers!) are amazed when the diagonals of a parallelogram or rectangle are not
ines of symmetry. Similarly, many expect mid-
egments of all parallelograms to serve as lines
of symmetry and are surprised when an angle of
90° does not work as an angle of rotation for all
parallelograms. Using Sketchpad to discover what
works for which parallelograms imprints the rela-
ionships in our students' memories far better than
any list, table, or static drawing ever has.

The S Files helps students notice details about
igures that alter their symmetries. Although this
activity may not be appropriate for beginners,
we feel it has helped improve the performance
of our students on standardized tests because
hese tests often contain questions involving
such figures.

Kids find **Alphabet Symmetry** lots of fun. The
extension promotes creativity, and students love
to share their designs.

Symmetric Patterns in a Hexagon is also
popular. Some kids really get carried away with
it, while others struggle a bit at first. Being
shown a sample solution helps some students get
started. We have seen much improvement in
kids' visual skills simply as a result of doing this
project themselves and testing the sketches of
other students.

The highlight of this unit for our kids each
year is the project **Make Me Symmetric.** This
project has been successful at our school with all
grade and skill levels. We have found that working in pairs works very well for this project.
Every year, both the students and teachers are
astounded at its overwhelming success. Students
make terrific gains in both their mathematical
skills and their self-confidence. A phenomenon
that shouldn't surprise us is that some of the
most creative projects are done by students who
don't usually lead the math class. In fact, the
poorest calculator or logician often has the best
project! It is also gratifying that someone like
John G. seems to emerge in every class—a kid
who gets so enthralled that he becomes the
"Animation Expert" and thrives on helping
classmates achieve the effects they desire in particular sketches. The students are always very
proud of the products they are able to create, and
rightly so. They often come back to visit our
classrooms, even a couple of years later, to
remind us of the working windshield wipers on
the animated car they made or the reaction of
their classmates when bees danced across the
screen in their sketch. "I had no idea I could
draw like that!" they often exclaim when looking
at their finished product. The mathematics they
learn while doing this project amazes us as well.

Be sure to cover the **Animation Tours** in the
Tours unit before students start their projects. A
little time spent by students in learning the

basics of animation will go a long way toward producing confidence and daring. It also prevents their asking you the same questions many times. A teacher demonstration that includes examples of student symmetry projects is a good motivator to get things off to a solid start. Kids always come in before and after school to perfect their figure or its animation. This project is a motivator for almost every single child!

Prerequisite Mathematical Terms and Concepts

- *point, segment, polygon, polygon interior, vertex*

- names and properties of quadrilaterals, right angles and straight angles, sum of measures of central angles of a circle

Recommended Sketchpad Proficiency

- Basic knowledge of the freehand tools.

- Use of the Symmetry and Transformations Quick Reference Guide, found at the end of this unit, is suggested.

- Doing the Quadrilaterals unit prior to this one would be beneficial; otherwise, you may want to use specific sketches from that unit as student questions arise.

Essential Vocabulary

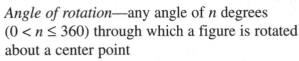

Angle of rotation—any angle of *n* degrees $(0 < n \leq 360)$ through which a figure is rotated about a center point

Center of rotation—a point about which a figure can be rotated

Line of symmetry—a line or segment that separates a figure into two halves that are mirror images of each other

Midsegment—a segment connecting the midpoints of two sides of a polygon

Reflection symmetry—symmetry in which a line can be drawn that separates the given figure into two halves that are mirror images of each other

Rotation symmetry—symmetry in which a figure can be rotated about a center point by an angle of rotation so that it lies exactly atop its original position

Symmetry—balance; correspondence of parts of a figure on opposite sides of a point, line, or plane

Instructions for Teacher Demonstrations

In each unit, we have included sketches and guidelines for demonstrations the teacher can use to introduce the material to the whole class before students attempt the various activities independently. They include the introduction of relevant mathematical vocabulary and concepts as well as appropriate Sketchpad skills. Often there are one or two activities that you will feel comfortable assigning to your students with very little guidance beforehand. In this unit, for example, **Mirrors and Reflection** works fine as an exploratory introduction to symmetry and requires very little technical expertise. On the other hand, one or more activities in each unit are designed to maximize guided discovery by the students. For these activities, a careful teacher demonstration will focus the students' attention on targeted mathematical concepts and prevent distractions due to lack of Sketchpad proficiency. In this unit, **Reflection and Rotation Symmetry** is designed to follow such a demonstration. Instructions are included later in these notes, along with answers for this guided discovery activity, for your convenience. Of course, you may want to use portions or adaptations of the demonstration before other activities; certainly, you will want to preview activities to be sure they are appropriate for the mathematical and Sketchpad skill levels of your students. In this Symmetry unit, at least a brief teacher demonstration is essential for success with most of the activities. Not only are the mathematical concepts new, but several Sketchpad skills that may be new to your students are also required in each activity. This situation calls for more preparation and practice than is necessary with most topics. Even with careful demonstrations, many students will forget one or more steps when they try for the first time, for example, to reflect a figure themselves at the computer. You need to show several examples and then have a student sit at the computer while another student gives verbal instructions at the close of the teacher demonstration.

We find it very valuable to solicit student suggestions during the demonstrations. In the rotation demonstration, for example, a student invariably first suggests trying an angle of rotation of 60° for the equilateral triangle. Errors like this stimulate thought, result in lively class discussion, and provide many opportunities for guided discovery.

You may find the Symmetry and Transformations Quick Reference Guide, found at the end of this unit, helpful in preparing for the symmetry demonstrations.

Reflection and Rotation Symmetry Activity

Exploring Reflection Symmetry

"Symmetry Demos" 1–6 are pages in the **Symmetry Demo.gsp** sketch.

1. Discuss *symmetry, line of symmetry,* and *reflection symmetry.* Demonstrate and discuss the following Sketchpad steps as you show "Symmetry Demo 1."

   - Mark a segment as a mirror.

   - Select a figure using a selection marquee.

   - Reflect the figure over the mirror. (Discuss with students what they think the resulting figure will look like before reflecting.)

- Drag parts of each design and discuss the effects of the changes.

2. Discuss testing a segment as a line of symmetry for a given figure. Demonstrate and discuss the following Sketchpad steps, using "Symmetry Demo 2."

   - Mark the dashed segment as a mirror.

   - Construct the polygon interior on one side of the segment.

   - Select the polygon interior and reflect it over the mirror.

   - Drag a vertex to show that the segment is a line of symmetry when the trapezoid is isosceles.

3. Using "Symmetry Demo 3," demonstrate constructing your own segments or lines to test figures for reflection symmetry.

   - Construct the midpoint of any side of the triangle and the segment connecting that midpoint to the opposite vertex.

   - Select the segment you have constructed and test your segment as a line of symmetry for the triangle.

   - Drag parts of the triangle and discuss the effects of the changes. Compare the results with those in "Symmetry Demo 2." (Be sure students observe that the segment is a line of symmetry because the triangle remains equilateral, unlike the arbitrary trapezoid in "Symmetry Demo 2," which must be manipulated to be isosceles.)

4. Demonstrate creating an original figure that has a line of symmetry.

   - Open a new sketch and, using the **Segment** tool ☐, draw a segment on the screen.

   - Use the **Segment** tool ☐ to draw a design on one side of the original segment.

   - Mark the original segment as a mirror.

- Using a selection marquee, select the design you drew.

- Reflect the design over the mirror.

- Drag parts of the design to show that any changes made on one side of the mirror move in the same way on the other side of the mirror.

Exploring Rotation Symmetry

1. Discuss *symmetry, angle of rotation, center of rotation,* and *rotation symmetry.* Demonstrate and discuss testing a figure for rotation symmetry as you show "Symmetry Demo 4" and "Symmetry Demo 5."

   - In "Symmetry Demo 4," select the shaded polygon interior, then rotate.

   - In "Symmetry Demo 5," select an entire figure using a selection marquee when the figure is not shaded, then rotate.

   - Test a figure for a particular angle of rotation (e.g., 30° as test angle).

2. Demonstrate and discuss testing a figure for rotation symmetry. Demonstrate the following Sketchpad skills as you show "Symmetry Demo 6."

   - Mark the point as a center.

   - Select a figure to rotate, using both methods (as in "Symmetry Demo 4" and "Symmetry Demo 5").

   - Rotate a figure by a given angle (show rotations of 90° and 180°).

   - Find the angle(s) of rotation for a figure that makes the figure lie exactly atop its original position (take student suggestions until they find 120° and 240°).

Tip: We have found it helpful to place a tick mark on one edge of the figure so that when the figure is rotated by an angle that makes it fall exactly atop its original position, it is obvious to the student that the figure has moved. See

below. Of course, you must select the tick mark before rotating the figure.

3. Demonstrate and discuss creating an origina figure that has rotation symmetry.

   - Open a new sketch and design a small, irregular polygon using the **Segment** tool ⟋.

   - Point out that a user may rotate a figure either by selecting only segments and points or by constructing the polygon inte rior and rotating.

   - Mark a point as a center (one of the lowe vertices of the polygon often works well) and rotate the figure.

4. Review the sequence for rotating a figure.

   - Select the polygon (remind students of the tick mark suggestion).

   - Go to the Transform menu, choose **Rotate** and make sure the **Fixed Angle** option is chosen in the dialog box.

   - Type in the desired angle of rotation.

   - Repeat the rotation by returning to the Transform menu as many times as needed

5. Demonstrate writing a student name on a sketch, using the **Text** tool Ⓐ.

   You'll find examples of student sketches in the folders **Student Reflection Sketches** and **Student Rotation Sketches.** These folders are in the **Symmetry** folder. You may want to show students these sketches to give them some ideas for their own sketches.

Writing Prompts

Ask students to choose a topic below and write a short paper, including sketches created with Sketchpad.

- Symmetry in Nature
- Symmetry in Quadrilaterals
- Symmetry in Regular Polygons
- Questions I Have About Symmetry

Examples of Student Work

Symmetry Project: Symmetric Patterns in a Hexagon

2a.   b.   c.   d.   e.   f.

Symmetry Project: Make Me Symmetric

By Alexis McLean

Ribbit Frog
This figure has one line of symmetry.

Rotating Roses
By Mary Forman and Alice B. Cox

This figure has angles of rotation of 60°, 120°, 180°, 240°, and 300°.

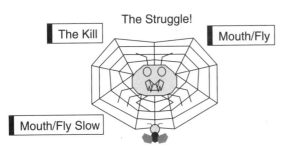

The Struggle!

The Kill

Mouth/Fly

Mouth/Fly Slow

This figure has one line of symmetry.

Bumble the Bee

Wings

Antennae

This figure has one line of symmetry.

Let's Boogie!

The Fishermen

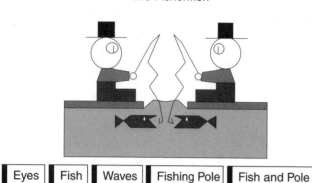

| Eyes | Fish | Waves | Fishing Pole | Fish and Pole |

Sunflower

Twinkle

This figure has angles of rotation of 45, 90, 135, 180, 225, 270, and 315 degrees.

Love Your Planet

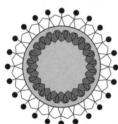

This figure has 12, 24, 36, 48, 60, 72, 84, 96, 108, 120, 132, 144, 156, 168, 180, 192, 204, 216, 228, 240, 252, 264, 276, 288, 300, 312, 324, 336, and 348 degree rotational symmetry.

Kaleidoscope

This figure has 90, 180, and 270 degree rotational symmetry.

Rotate

Answers for Reflection and Rotation Symmetry Activity

4. a. no   b. none   c. trapezoid
   d. yes   e. 2   f. rhombus
   g.

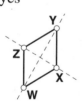

6. a. 5   b.

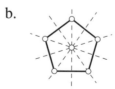

8. a. yes   b. 120°, 240°, 360°   c. yes
   d. 180°, 360°

10. a. yes   b. 60°, 120°, 180°, 240°, 300°, 360°   c. yes
    d. 90°, 180°, 270°, 360°

12. a. yes
    d. 180°, 360°
    g. yes

b. 2
e. no
h. 180°, 360°

c. yes
f. none

Answers for Symmetry Wrap-Up

1. a. no
    d. no

b. yes
e. yes

c. no
f. yes

2. a.

b.

c.

3. a. no, yes

b. no, yes

c. yes, yes

    d. no, no

e. no, yes

f. yes, yes

4. a. Answers will vary. Possible answer: square.
    b. Answers will vary. Possible answer: parallelogram.
    c. Answers will vary. Possible answer: regular polygon with five or more sides.

Mirrors and Reflection

1. Open a new sketch.

2. Construct a segment.

3. Double-click on the segment to mark it as a mirror.

4. Construct a polygon on one side of the segment (see example).

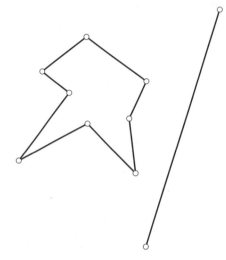

5. Using the **Selection Arrow** tool ⬚, drag a selection marquee around the polygon to select it.

6. Reflect the polygon.

7. Drag any vertex of the polygon. Describe what happens.

_____

_____

_____

8. Drag the mirror. Describe what happens.

_____

_____

_____

Reflection and Rotation Symmetry

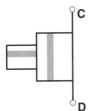  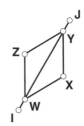 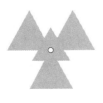

Use Sketchpad to explore reflection and rotation symmetry.

1. Open the sketch **Symmetry Exp.gsp** and go to the page "Symmetry Exp 1."

2. Follow the instructions in the sketch.

3. Go to the page "Symmetry Exp 2."

4. Follow the instructions in the sketch and answer these questions.

   a. Is the dashed segment $\overline{GH}$ a line of symmetry for quadrilateral **ADCB**? _____

   b. How many lines of symmetry do you think quadrilateral **ADCB** has? _____

   c. What kind of quadrilateral is **ADCB**? _____
      You can measure the angles and sides if needed to identify the quadrilateral.

   d. Is the dashed segment $\overline{IJ}$ a line of symmetry for quadrilateral **WXYZ**? _____

   e. How many lines of symmetry do you think quadrilateral **WXYZ** has? _____

   f. What kind of quadrilateral is **WXYZ**? _____
      You can measure the angles and sides if needed to identify the quadrilateral.

   g. Sketch quadrilateral **WXYZ** and show all its lines of symmetry here.

5. Go to the page "Symmetry Exp 3."

6. Follow the instructions in the sketch and answer these questions.

   a. How many lines of symmetry does the regular pentagon have? _____

   b. Sketch the regular pentagon and show all its lines of symmetry here.

7. Go to the page "Symmetry Exp 4."

8. Follow the instructions in the sketch and answer these questions.

   a. Does figure E have rotation symmetry? _____

   b. If so, list the angle(s) of rotation that make the figure lie atop its original position. _____

   c. Does figure F have rotation symmetry? _____

   d. If so, list the angle(s) of rotation that make the figure lie atop its original position. _____

9. Go to the page "Symmetry Exp 5."

10. Follow the instructions in the sketch and answer these questions.

    a. Does the regular hexagon in figure G have rotation symmetry? _____

    b. If so, list the angle(s) of rotation that make the figure lie atop its original position. _____

    c. Does figure H have rotation symmetry? _____

    d. If so, list the angle(s) of rotation that make the figure lie atop its original position. _____

11. Go to the page "Symmetry Exp 6."

12. Follow the instructions in the sketch and answer these questions.

    a. Does figure I have reflection symmetry? _____

    b. If so, how many lines of symmetry does it have? _____

    c. Does figure I have rotation symmetry? _____

    d. If so, list the angle(s) of rotation that make the figure lie atop its original position. _____

    e. Does figure J have reflection symmetry? _____

    f. If so, how many lines of symmetry does it have? _____

    g. Does figure J have rotation symmetry? _____

    h. If so, list the angle(s) of rotation that make the figure lie atop its original position. _____

Diagonals in Parallelograms

1. Open **Parallelogram Sym Diagonals.gsp**.

2. Click on the *Show Diagonal AD* button in the sketch to show the diagonal between points **A** and **D** and the polygon interior for △ADC.

3. Test diagonal $\overline{AD}$ as a line of symmetry for parallelogram **ABDC** by marking $\overline{AD}$ as a mirror, then reflecting the polygon interior of △ADC over the mirror. (See the Symmetry and Transformations Quick Reference Guide, if needed, for help.)

4. Drag your parallelogram into different types of parallelograms. Make sure to drag parallelogram **ABDC** so that it looks like a rectangle, a rhombus, and a square by dragging vertex **A**, **B**, **C**, or **D**.

5. Describe parallelogram **ABDC** when diagonal $\overline{AD}$ is a line of symmetry.

_____

_____

6. Click on the *Hide Diagonal AD and Interiors* button in your sketch to hide $\overline{AD}$ and the polygon interiors.

7. Click on the *Show Diagonal CB* button in the sketch.

8. Test diagonal $\overline{CB}$ as a line of symmetry for parallelogram **ABDC** by marking $\overline{CB}$ as a mirror, then reflecting the polygon interior of △**ABC** over the mirror.

9. Drag your parallelogram so that it looks like different types of parallelograms. Make sure to drag parallelogram **ABDC** into a rectangle, a rhombus, and a square by dragging vertex **A**, **B**, **C**, or **D**.

10. Describe parallelogram **ABDC** when diagonal $\overline{CB}$ is a line of symmetry.

_____

_____

11. What conclusion(s) can you draw about the diagonals of a parallelogram as lines of symmetry?

_____

_____

_____

Midsegments in Parallelograms

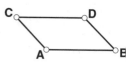

1. Open **Parallelogram Sym Midsegs.gsp**.

2. Click on the *Show Midsegment FE* button to show the midsegment between midpoints **F** and **E** and the polygon interior for parallelogram **FEDC**.

3. Test midsegment $\overline{FE}$ as a line of symmetry for parallelogram **ABDC** by marking $\overline{FE}$ a a mirror, then reflecting the polygon interior of parallelogram **FEDC** over the mirror. (See the Symmetry and Transformations Quick Reference Guide, if needed, for help.)

4. Drag your parallelogram into different types of parallelograms. Make sure to drag parallelogram **ABDC** so that it looks like a rectangle, a rhombus, and a square by dragging vertex **A**, **B**, **C**, or **D**.

5. Describe parallelogram **ABDC** when midsegment $\overline{FE}$ is a line of symmetry.

   _____

   _____

6. Click on the *Hide FE and Interiors* button in your sketch to hide midsegment **FE** and the polygon interiors.

7. Click on the *Show Midsegment GH* button to show the midsegment between midpoints **G** and **H**.

8. Test midsegment $\overline{GH}$ as a line of symmetry for parallelogram **ABDC** by marking $\overline{GH}$ as a mirror, then reflecting the polygon interior of parallelogram **AGHC** over the mirror

9. Drag your parallelogram so that it looks like different types of parallelograms. Make sure to drag parallelogram **ABDC** into a rectangle, a rhombus, and a square by dragging vertex **A**, **B**, **C**, or **D**.

10. Describe parallelogram **ABDC** when midsegment $\overline{GH}$ is a line of symmetry.

    _____

    _____

11. What conclusion(s) can you draw about the midsegments of a parallelogram as lines of symmetry?

    _____

    _____

    _____

Rotation Symmetry in Parallelograms

1. Open the sketch **Parallelogram Center.gsp.** The polygon interior of parallelogram **ABDC** has been constructed, and it can be rotated about the point **center.** The angle of rotation can be changed by dragging point **X** in the angle **XYZ**.

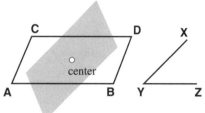

2. Drag point **X** to rotate the polygon interior. Find all angles of rotation less than 360° for which the polygon interior lies exactly atop parallelogram **ABDC**.

3. Does the general parallelogram displayed in this sketch have rotation symmetry for the following angles of rotation?

    90° _____   180° _____   270° _____

4. Drag parallelogram **ABDC** into a rectangle by dragging vertex **A**, **B**, **D**, or **C**. Does the rectangle displayed in this sketch have rotation symmetry for the following angles of rotation?

    90° _____   180° _____   270° _____

5. Drag parallelogram **ABDC** into a rhombus by dragging vertex **A**, **B**, **D**, or **C**. Does the rhombus displayed in this sketch have rotation symmetry for the following angles of rotation?

    90° _____   180° _____   270° _____

6. Drag parallelogram **ABDC** into a square by dragging vertex **A**, **B**, **D**, or **C**. Does the square displayed in this sketch have rotation symmetry for the following angles of rotation?

    90° _____   180° _____   270° _____

7. What conjecture(s) can you make about rotation symmetry in parallelograms?

    _____

    _____

The S Files

1. Open the sketch **The S Files.gsp**.

For questions 2–4, use Sketchpad to explore reflection and rotation symmetries in the figures in this sketch.

2. Compare the reflection and rotation symmetries in the figure on the left to the symmetries of a square.

square

_____

_____

_____

3. Compare the reflection and rotation symmetries in the figure on the left to the symmetries of a regular octagon.

regular octagon

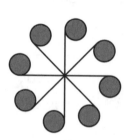

_____

_____

_____

4. Compare the reflection and rotation symmetries in the figure on the left to those of an isosceles triangle and to those of an equilateral triangle.

isosceles triangle   equilateral triangle

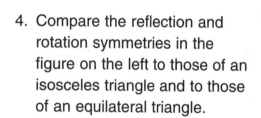  

_____

_____

_____

Alphabet Symmetry

Work with a partner or group to construct the 26 capital letters of our alphabet on the Sketchpad grid. Then classify them according to the reflection and rotation symmetries they have. Organize your results into a table.

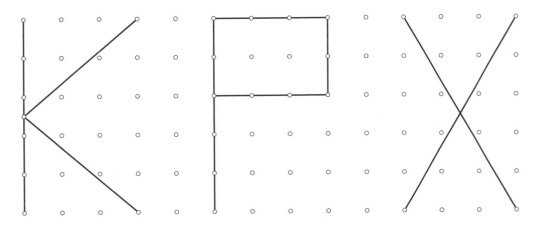

Extension: Design your own alphabet using Sketchpad so that every letter has reflection or rotation symmetry. You may want to change some of the traditional letters as little as possible (see the example), or you may want to completely design your own alphabet.

Example: For the letter *P*, you might choose to construct a design similar to one of those shown below.

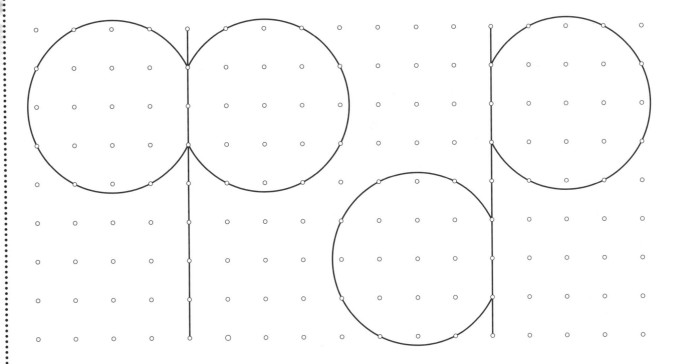

Symmetric Patterns in a Hexagon

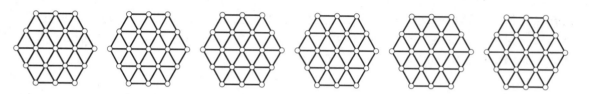

1. Open the sketch **Hexagon Symmetry.gsp.** You will see a sketch containing six congruent hexagons.

    To shade the inside of a figure using Sketchpad, you need to create the polygon interior of the polygon. To do this, using the **Selection Arrow** tool ⬚, click on the vertices of the polygon in clockwise or counterclockwise order, go to the Construct menu, and choose **Hexagon Interior** or the appropriate variation.

2. Shade one or more small triangles so that the completed design has the following reflection symmetry:

    a. Hexagon A has a vertical line of symmetry and no other.

    b. Hexagon B has a horizontal line of symmetry and no other.

    c. Hexagon C has both vertical and horizontal lines of symmetry.

    Shade in small triangles with a total area one-fourth that of the hexagonal region so that the completed design has the following rotation symmetry:

    d. Hexagon D has 180° rotation symmetry.

    e. Hexagon E has 60° rotation symmetry.

    f. Hexagon F has 120° rotation symmetry.

3. Test your answers to step 2 using reflections and rotations.

    To reflect an object, you must first mark a mirror. To do this, select a segment or a line, go to the Transform menu, and choose **Mark Mirror.** Then select the figure you wish to reflect, go to the Transform menu, and choose **Reflect.**

    To rotate an object, you must select a point using Sketchpad, go to the Transform menu, and choose **Mark Center.** Then select the figure you wish to rotate, go to the Transform menu, and choose **Rotate.** Enter an angle of rotation.

4. Put your name on your sketch and print out a copy to hand in.

Extension: Copy one of the original hexagons onto a new sketch. Shade triangles to create another design with both reflection and rotation symmetry. Write a statement on your sketch that tells what line(s) of symmetry it has and the angle(s) of rotation. Put your name on your sketch and print out a copy.

Make Me Symmetric

1. Use Sketchpad to create a figure with reflection symmetry. You must create a mirror and use reflection to give your figure at least one line of symmetry. Include a title, your name, and a statement describing the reflection symmetry of your figure.

2. Use Sketchpad to create a figure with rotation symmetry. Include a title, your name, and a statement describing the rotation symmetry of your figure.

Note: You can animate your figure by using the Sketchpad Animation buttons. If you choose to include Animation buttons, you will need to save the animated version on a disk.

The Clown

By Sharman Ringland and Alexis McLean

This figure has one line of symmetry.

1. Find an example of reflection or rotation symmetry in the real world—a leaf, a tile pattern, the front of a building, or the like. Open a new sketch and create a Sketchpad version of the object.

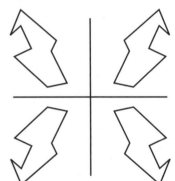

2. Create a figure with two lines of symmetry. Drag your figure to discover whether such a figure will *sometimes, always,* or *never* have rotation symmetry.

   Now try to create a figure with three lines of symmetry. Explore its rotation symmetry. Can you make a general statement about the relationship between the number of lines of reflection and the number of angles of rotation in these figures?

3. Read about snowflakes. Create your own version of a Sketchpad snowflake using reflections or rotations.

4. Use Sketchpad to create several polygons with different numbers of sides (first three, then four, five, and so on). Drag the vertices of each polygon so that it has reflection symmetry. After examining several such polygons, describe how the number of sides relates to the location of the line(s) of symmetry.

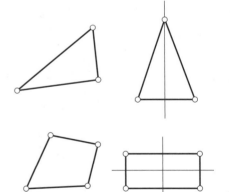

5. Open a new sketch and use the **Segment** tool ☑ to write your name. Reflect it over a line. Drag vertices to make it more interesting. Print a copy of your sketch.

Choose another word you think would make a nice visual image after it is reflected or rotated. Create your "picture word" using Sketchpad. Can you make your picture word show the meaning of the word as well?

6. Investigate lines of symmetry in a circle. How many are there? What do all such lines of symmetry have in common? What can you say about rotation symmetry in a circle? Drag to try circles of different sizes. What conjectures can you propose?

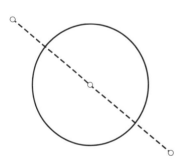

Reflection Symmetry

1. Is $\overline{XY}$ a line of symmetry? Write *yes* or *no*.

a. _____

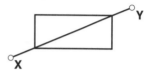

b. _____

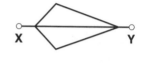

c. _____

d. _____

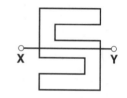

e. _____

f. _____

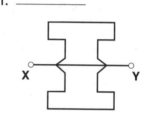

2. Draw all lines of symmetry for each figure. If the figure has no lines of symmetry, write *none*.

a. _____

b. _____

c. _____

Rotation Symmetry

3. Does each figure have 90° rotation symmetry? Does each figure have 180° rotation symmetry? Write *yes* or *no*. If *yes*, mark the center of rotation.

a. 90° _____
   180° _____

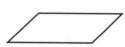

b. 90° _____
   180° _____

c. 90° _____
   180° _____

Geometry Activities for Middle School Students with The Geometer's Sketchpad
©2004 Key Curriculum Press

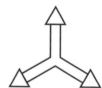
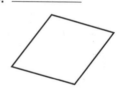
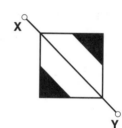

d. 90° _____   e. 90° _____   f. 90° _____
   180° _____   180° _____   180° _____

4. Draw a figure that has the rotation symmetry listed.

   a. 90° and 180°   b. 180° only   c. an angle of rotation
                                                      less than 90°

To mark a segment or line as a mirror (use the **Selection Arrow** tool)

1. Click on the line or segment.

2. Go to the Transform menu and choose **Mark Mirror.**

To reflect a figure over a mirror (use the **Selection Arrow** tool )

1. Mark a line or a segment as a mirror.

2. Select the figure.

3. Go to the Transform menu and choose **Reflect.**

To mark a point as a center (use the **Selection Arrow** tool)

1. Click on the point.

2. Go to the Transform menu and choose **Mark Center.**

To rotate a figure by a fixed angle (use the **Selection Arrow** tool)

1. Mark a point as a center.

2. Select the figure.

3. Go to the Transform menu and choose **Rotate.**

4. Choose **By Fixed Angle** in the dialog box.

5. Enter the angle measure.

6. Click Rotate.

To construct a segment between two existing points (use the **Selection Arrow** tool)

1. Click on the two points.

2. Go to the Construct menu and choose **Segment.**

A ◉

◉
B

To construct a polygon interior (use the **Selection Arrow** tool ⌧)

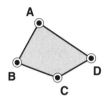

1. Click on the vertices of the polygon in order, either clockwise or counterclockwise.

2. Go to the Construct menu and choose **Polygon Interior.** (*Note:* Sketchpad will always refer to polygons by their specific names.)

To select a figure using a selection marquee (use the **Selection Arrow** tool ⌧)

1. Click above and to the left of the figure. Drag the mouse down and to the right until the dashed rectangle surrounds the figure.

2. Release the mouse button. All objects inside the rectangle should be selected.

To select the polygon interior of a polygon (use the **Selection Arrow** tool ⌧)

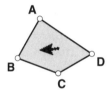

1. Click on the shaded area of the polygon.

To write your name(s) on a sketch and then print (use the **Text** tool Ⓐ)

Glenn and Chip

1. Double-click in a blank space to create a text box.

2. Type your name(s) in this box.

3. Go to the File menu and choose **Print.**

To measure segments or sides of polygons (use the **Selection Arrow** tool ⌧)

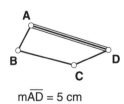

1. Click on the side or segment.

2. Go to the Measure menu and choose **Length.**

3. Drag the measurement to a different location, if needed.

$m\overline{AD} = 5$ cm

To measure angles (use the **Selection Arrow** tool 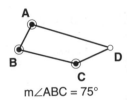)

1. Click on the three points that define the angle. (Make sure you click on the vertex second—for ∠**B**, click on **A**, **B**, and then **C** or click on **C**, **B**, and then **A**.)

2. Go to the Measure menu and choose **Angle**.

m∠ABC = 75°

To dilate a figure by a fixed ratio

1. Select an existing point or use the **Point** tool to construct a point for your center.

2. Go to the Transform menu and choose **Mark Center.**

3. Use a selection marquee to select the figure. Go to the Transform menu and choose **Dilate.**

4. When the Dilate dialog box appears, enter the scale factors. Click Dilate.

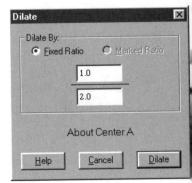

Dilate Dialog Box (Windows)

To dilate a figure by a marked ratio (use the **Selection Arrow** tool)

1. Click on a point to use as your center. Go to the Transform menu and choose **Mark Center.**

2. Construct two line segments in your sketch whose lengths show the ratio by which you wish to dilate. (Or select two line segments already in your sketch.)

3. Click on both segments. Go to the Transform menu and choose **Mark Segment Ratio.**

4. Use a selection marquee to select the figure. Go to the Transform menu and choose **Dilate.**

5. When the Dilate dialog box appears, click Dilate.

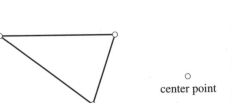

segments selected to mark ratio

center point

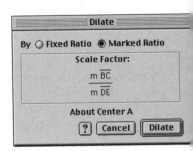

Dilate Dialog Box (Macintosh)

TRANSFORMATIONS

Commentary

The topic of transformations has received varying degrees of emphasis in middle school mathematics curricula in past decades. With increased use of computers in the classroom and workplace, however, the topic undoubtedly will receive increased attention at these grade levels. Investigating transformations fosters development of spatial reasoning and also builds a conceptual foundation for topics as varied as slope, trigonometric ratios, and fractals. As a significant bonus, middle school kids love this topic!

Ideally, students doing the activities in this unit will have some Sketchpad proficiency. If not, the teacher demonstrations should receive special emphasis. Doing the activities in the Symmetry unit prior to this unit would be beneficial as well.

The activities **Exploring Translations** and **Exploring Rotations** are designed as introductory explorations for students who are unfamiliar with these concepts. The second part of each of these activities leads students through an alternate Sketchpad method for performing the transformations. You may want to omit these portions for some students until they are proficient in using the first method. It may also be appropriate to use the activity **Mirrors and Reflection** from the Symmetry unit with students who are being introduced to this topic for the first time. Of course, class discussion is needed as a follow-up to these explorations to clarify the definitions of the transformations for all your students.

During the teacher demonstration for **Exploring Transformations with Freehand Tools,** you will need to show the use of the **Rotation** tool 🔄 with several figures. If students have trouble making the pre-image and image match exactly, lead them to discover how to make this happen by moving the center of rotation. Also, it is best to let students suggest an alternate set of transformations for moving the same pre-image to its image rather than just providing another solution for them. This teaching technique stimulates kids to visualize the results of various transformations in their minds and helps build confidence—even when several "undos" are needed before they are successful! We have found that this independent exploration helps students develop an accurate understanding of what happens to a figure during each kind of rigid transformation, an understanding that some fail to grasp when Sketchpad physically performs the transformation for them. Be sure students realize that a 90° rotation is in a counterclockwise direction, whereas a –90° rotation moves the figure clockwise. Student comments during these explorations are delightful: "No, no, we still gotta reflect—you got the fat leg on the skinny one!" and "That's not good enough. Move that center so the figures fit exactly!"

During the teacher demonstration for **Transformations on the Coordinate Grid,** you may want to show the students how to display coordinates of points with Sketchpad. However, we believe it is a good idea to have students at this level first name the coordinates themselves and then check their answers with Sketchpad. *Note:* In this activity, we have used the notation $\langle -5, 1 \rangle$ to express the transformation $(x, y) \rightarrow (x - 5, y + 3)$. This notation helps prevent students from confusing the translation with the coordinate $(-5, 1)$.

For **Glide Reflections,** you may choose to omit showing your students translating a figure by a marked vector. For some groups, you may want to show this at a later time, and for others, not at all. We have found it to be an alternative method that kids avoid if they do not understand it but utilize quite efficiently if they do. As always, adjust your instruction to fit the needs of your students.

As you introduce dilations to your students in **Dilations,** it is important to point out the difference between this type of transformation and the rigid transformations (isometries) they have previously encountered. Though most middle school kids are familiar with photo enlargements and scale drawings or other practical applications of dilations, most likely they have not encountered the concept formally in their mathematics classes and often miss the distinction unless it is emphasized. For some groups of students, it may be appropriate to postpone the introduction of dilating a figure by a marked ratio until the first method has been completely mastered. Note that a third method, using the **Dilation** tool ⌖, is also available with Sketchpad. This activity brings "oohs" and "ahas" from students and stimulates many independent, self-initiated explorations.

Before students do **Similar Figures,** they often need a review of several Sketchpad skills and a teacher demonstration in addition to an introduction to corresponding sides and angles. We have found a dramatic improvement among students' recall of the important concepts related to similar figures since we started using this activity in our classes.

Your students will likely encounter a challenge with **Mission: Matched Pairs.** We suggest letting students work in pairs or teams. Another alternative is to require only 10 correct solutions instead of all 13. Despite their struggles, most of our students are quite engaged by this project and exhibit a real sense of pride when they are successful with it.

The Name Game is relatively simple, and the kids love to exhibit their results. As you can imagine, some produce quite elaborate creations!

Before students do **Triangle Buddies,** we find it important to demonstrate selecting the point at the intersection of the side of the triangle and the new parallel line and then constructing

a new segment for each part of the original side. Point out to students that the measure of the length of a segment is the same as the distance between its two endpoints. Since measuring the distance between two points in this situation is a simpler maneuver with Sketchpad, you may want to encourage your students to use this method along with the **Calculate** command from the Measure menu to find the ratio of the corresponding sides in the newly formed triangles.

For **Go, Team, Go,** you may want to expand the choices for your students to include an athletic court at a neighborhood recreation facility or nearby university. We have also varied this project to allow a scale drawing of any athletic court or field (in this case, checking the accuracy of student sketches becomes a challenge!). Kids enjoy sharing their sketches. If all students are assigned the same court, a good follow-up activity is to have students observe that all their scale drawings are dilations of the same pre-image and, therefore, are all similar figures. You might have them find the scale factor between different groups' drawings. Working in pairs works well for this project.

If you wish to focus more on transformations, use the **Transform Me!** activity. For some classes, you can add polar vectors as an option. You'll find examples of student sketches in the folder **Student Trans Sketches.**

The results of **Golden Rectangle Survey** astound students every time we assign it. As long as the other three rectangles in their sketch are clearly *not* golden rectangles, more than 50% of the respondents to the survey always prefer their golden rectangle. You'll find many of your students quite eager to do more research and investigation on this topic. Be sure to discuss the questions listed in the Think It Over section of the project. Note that students will need to complete **Constructing a Golden Rectangle** (see Unit 7, Constructions) as part of this project.

If you do not include dilations in your Transformations unit, you should omit questions 4 through 9 in the **Transformations Wrap-Up;** questions 1 through 3 relate to rigid transformations.

The project **Make Me Symmetric,** found in the Symmetry unit of this book, makes a very nice assessment activity at the completion of the Symmetry and Transformations units for middle school students of all ages and abilities.

Several of the activities in the Constructions unit (Unit 7) of this book involve transformations and/or similar polygons. Try doing **Constructing a Golden Rectangle, Constructing a Pantograph, Constructing a Binary Tree Fractal, Constructing a Sierpiński Gasket Fractal,** or **Constructing a Dragon Fractal** with your students. We have used each of these with great success!

Prerequisite Mathematical Terms and Concepts

polygon interior, origin, coordinates of a point, horizontal, vertical, x-axis, y-axis, ratio, proportion

congruent figures, points on a coordinate plane, angles and angle measures, corresponding sides, corresponding angles, scale factor

Recommended Sketchpad Proficiency

Basic knowledge of the freehand tools; some experience with Sketchpad is helpful.

Use of the Symmetry and Transformations Quick Reference Guide (found at the end of the Symmetry unit) is suggested.

Doing the Symmetry unit prior to this one would be beneficial; otherwise, you may want to use specific sketches from that unit as student questions arise.

Essential Vocabulary

Angle of rotation—any angle of *n* degrees (0 < *n* < 360) by which a figure is rotated around a point

Dilation—a transformation that shrinks or enlarges a figure

Glide reflection—a transformation that is a combination of a reflection and a translation

Image—a figure obtained through a transformation of a given figure

Isometry—movement of a figure so that the position of the figure changes but its size and shape do not

Line of reflection—line over which a pre-image is reflected

Pre-image—the original figure in a transformation

Reflection—a transformation that yields a figure that is a mirror image of the given figure

Rigid transformation (isometry)—movement of a figure so that the position of the figure changes but its size and shape do not; see also *reflection, rotation, translation*

Rotation—a transformation that rotates a figure a certain number of degrees about a point

Scale factor—the ratio of corresponding sides in two similar figures

Similar polygons—two or more polygons that have all pairs of corresponding angles congruent and the same ratio for the lengths of all pairs of corresponding sides

Transformation—changing of a figure, as by a *reflection, rotation, translation,* or *dilation*

Translation—a transformation that moves all points in a figure by a given distance and in a given direction

Vector—a directed distance; can be used to define a translation

Instructions for Teacher Demonstrations

In each unit, we have included sketches and guidelines for demonstrations the teacher can use to introduce the material to the whole class before students attempt the various activities independently. They include the introduction of relevant mathematical vocabulary and concepts as well as appropriate Sketchpad skills. Often, there are one or several activities you will feel comfortable assigning to your students with very little guidance beforehand. In this unit, for example, the activities **Exploring Translations** and **Exploring Rotations** work fine as exploratory introductions to transformations and require very little technical expertise. On the other hand, one or more activities in each unit are designed to maximize guided discovery by the students. For these activities, a careful teacher demonstration will focus students' attention on targeted mathematical concepts and prevent distractions due to lack of Sketchpad proficiency. In this unit, the activities **Exploring Transformations with Freehand Tools, Transformations on the Coordinate Grid, Dilations,** and **Similar Figures** are designed to follow such a demonstration. The instructions are given in these notes. You may want to use portions or adaptations of the demonstrations before doing other activities; certainly, you will want to preview activities to be sure they are appropriate for the mathematical and Sketchpad skill levels of your students.

If you choose to have your students work through several of the activities in this unit, you may want to show them the following shortcuts for marking mirrors and centers:

- To mark a mirror, simply double-click on the line or segment you wish to designate as the mirror.

- To mark a center, you can double-click on the point you wish to designate as the center.

It has been our experience with middle school students that it is best to postpone the use of shortcuts until the students fully understand the steps that each shortcut replaces.

You may find the Symmetry and Transformations Quick Reference Guide (at the end of the Symmetry unit) helpful in preparing for the transformations demonstrations.

Exploring Transformations with Freehand Tools

"Trans Demos" 1–5 are pages in the sketch **Trans Demo.gsp.**

1. Discuss *transformations* and *translations.* Demonstrate the following Sketchpad skills as you show "Trans Demo 1":

   - Select the figure and copy it.

   - Paste the image and change its color or shade.

   - Use the **Selection Arrow** tool ![arrow] to drag (translate) the image. Discuss with students the relationship of the image and the pre-image.

2. Discuss *reflections* and *lines of reflection.* Demonstrate the following Sketchpad skills as you show "Trans Demo 2":

   - Mark a segment as a mirror.

   - Select a figure, using a selection marquee.

   - Reflect the figure over the mirror. Before reflecting, discuss with the students what they think the resulting figure will look like.

   - Drag the mirror and discuss the effects.

3. Discuss *rotations.* Demonstrate the following Sketchpad skills as you show "Trans Demo 3":

   - Construct a point in the sketch and mark it as a center. (Discuss with the students where they think the center should be to make the pre-image match the rotated image.)

- Rotate the figure, using the **Rotation** tool 🔘.

- Drag the center and discuss the effects. (You will have to use the **Selection Arrow** tool 🔘 to drag the center.)

4. Show how different transformations of a pre-image may be used to create the same image, using "Trans Demo 4" (e.g., create a rotated image and then show this same result by using two reflections).

- Double-click on the *Show Center* button.

- Mark the point as a center.

- Select the pre-image and rotate by an angle of 60°.

- Change the shade or color to clearly identify the image.

- Double-click on the *Show Mirror 1* button.

- Mark the segment as a mirror.

- Select the pre-image and reflect.

- Double-click on the *Show Mirror 2* button.

- Mark the new segment as a mirror.

- Select the reflected image and reflect.

Transformations on the Coordinate Grid

Rigid Transformations

1. Review *transformations, reflections,* and *lines of reflection.* Demonstrate the following Sketchpad skills as you show "Trans Demo 5":

- Mark one of the axes as a mirror.

- Select a polygon interior and the vertices.

- Reflect the polygon over the mirror. Before you do the reflection, discuss with students what they think the image will look like.

2. Discuss *rotations.* Demonstrate the following Sketchpad skills as you show "Trans Demo 5":

- Select a point (one of the vertices of the polygon or the origin) and mark it as a center.

- Select the polygon and the vertices.

- Choose **Rotate** from the Transform menu, enter an angle measure (we suggest 90° or 180°), and rotate the polygon. Discuss with students what they think the image will look like before you do the rotation.

3. Discuss *translations,* especially notation, such as ⟨4, 2⟩. Demonstrate the following Sketchpad skills, using "Trans Demo 5":

- Select the vertices and the polygon interior.

- Choose **Translate** from the Transform menu.

- In the dialog box, enter appropriate horizontal and vertical measures (make sure By Rectangular Vector is chosen) and translate the polygon.

Dilations

"Dilate Demos" 1–4 are pages in the sketch **Dilate Demo.gsp**.

1. Review *transformations* and *similar polygons.* Use "Dilate Demo 1" to illustrate a pair of similar polygons.

   a. Pairs of corresponding sides

   - Select a pair of corresponding sides. Note that order is important.

   - Choose **Ratio** from the Measure menu.

   - Repeat for each pair of corresponding sides to show that the ratio is the same for each pair.

   - Drag any part of any figure and discuss the effects.

b. Pairs of corresponding angles

- Select the three points that define one of the interior angles in quadrilateral **BARN**, in clockwise or counterclockwise order.

- Choose **Angle** from the Measure menu.

- Measure the corresponding angle in quadrilateral **SILO**. Compare the measures of the corresponding angles.

- Repeat for each pair of corresponding angles.

- Drag any part of any figure and discuss the effects.

2. Define a *dilation* and explain how it is different from an isometry. Review *corresponding sides* and *corresponding angles*. Review *ratios,* especially the 1:1 ratio for equal measures. Demonstrate the following Sketchpad skills, using "Dilate Demo 2":

a. Dilate a figure using a scale factor.

- Select point **S** and choose **Mark Center** from the Transform menu.

- Using a selection marquee, select hexagon **TAYLOR** and choose **Dilate** from the Transform menu.

- For the Scale Factor, enter 1 for the top (numerator) box and 2 for the bottom (denominator) box.

- Drag any part of any figure and discuss the effects.

b. Find the ratio of two corresponding sides.

- Select a pair of corresponding sides in the pre-image and the image. Note that order is important.

- Choose **Ratio** from the Measure menu.

- Repeat for each pair of corresponding sides.

- Drag any part of any figure and discuss the effects.

c. Compare the measures of corresponding angles.

- Select the three points that define one of the interior angles in hexagon **TAYLOR**, in clockwise or counterclockwise order.

- Choose **Angle** from the Measure menu.

- Repeat for the corresponding angle of the image.

- Compare the angle measures.

- Repeat for each pair of corresponding angles.

- Drag any part of any figure and discuss the effects.

3. Dilate a figure by a marked ratio. Demonstrate the following Sketchpad skills, using "Dilate Demo 3":

- Select point **D** and choose **Mark Center** from the Transform menu.

- Select $\overline{LM}$ and then $\overline{JK}$. Choose **Mark Ratio** from the Transform menu.

- Using a selection marquee, select pentagon **MARGE** and choose **Dilate** from the Transform menu.

- Choose **By Marked Ratio** in the dialog box.

- Drag **K** in the sketch and discuss how the figure changes.

- Discuss or demonstrate the ratio of corresponding sides and corresponding angles.

- Drag any part of any figure and discuss the effects.

4. Dilate a figure using the **Dilation** tool ▨. Demonstrate the following Sketchpad skills, using "Dilate Demo 4":

- Select point **D** and choose **Mark Center** from the Transform menu.

- Press and hold down the mouse button on the **Selection Arrow** tool ▨. Drag to the right and choose the **Dilation** tool ▨.

- Select the entire figure **PAUL**, using a selection marquee, and drag to show the effect of using the **Dilation** tool ⬚.

Similar Figures

1. Discuss *polygons.* Review the meaning of *ratio.* Demonstrate the following Sketchpad skills, using "Similar Demo":

   a. Measure an angle.
   - Select the three points that define the angle, in clockwise or counterclockwise order.
   - Choose **Angle** from the Measure menu.

   b. Find the ratio of two segments.
   - Select the segments.
   - Choose **Ratio** from the Measure menu.

   c. Change the name of a measure (a name often needs shortening).

2. Discuss corresponding sides and corresponding angles in a pair of polygons.

Using "Similar Demo," have students identify the following:

- Each pair of corresponding sides in quadrilaterals **BARN** and **SILO**.

- Each pair of corresponding angles in quadrilaterals **BARN** and **SILO**.

Writing Prompts

Ask students to choose a topic below and write a short paper, including sketches created with Sketchpad.

- Flip, Slide, and Turn—The Basics of Transformations
- Groovin' on the Grid (Transformations on the Coordinate Plane)
- Similarity Simplified
- Up, Down, and All Around— Transformations in the Real World
- If I Were a Transformation

Examples of Student Work

The Name Game

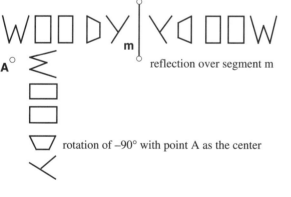

reflection over segment m

rotation of –90° with point A as the center

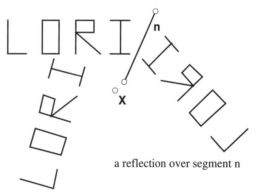

a reflection over segment n

a rotation of 75° with X as the center

Answers for Transformations on the Coordinate Grid Activity

2.
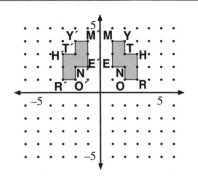

6.
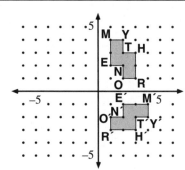

4. **M′** (−1, 4)   **R′** (−3, 1)

8. **M′** (4, −1)   **R′** (1, −3)

10.
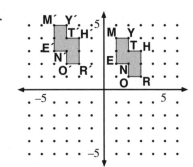

14.
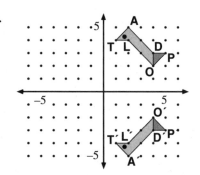

12. **M′** (−4, 5)   **R′** (−2, 2)

16. **A′** (2, −5)   **P′** (5, −3)

18.
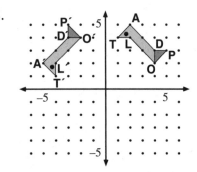

22.
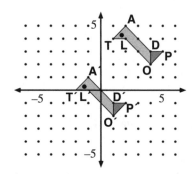

20. **A′** (−5, 2)   **P′** (−3, 5)

24. **A′** (−1, 1)   **P′** (2, −1)

Answers for Dilations Activity

3. 0.75

4. Each side in the image is three-fourths as long as the corresponding side in the pre-image. Alternative answer: The ratio of the measures of the lengths of each pair of corresponding sides is 0.75.

5. They are equal.

6. a. They are equal.   b. 1.00, or 1 : 1

7. a. 1.25   b. 1.00, or 1 : 1

8. The ratio of the measures of the lengths of each pair of corresponding sides will
    be 0.67, or 2 : 3. The ratio of the measures of each pair of corresponding angles
    is 1.00, or 1 : 1.

12. Both ratios are 0.5.

13. yes

14. They are equal.

15. a. They are equal.   b. 1.00, or 1 : 1

    c. Yes. The ratio of the measures of the lengths of every pair of corresponding
        sides is the same. The measures of every pair of corresponding angles are the
        same.

16. a. When $\overline{EF}$ is shorter than $\overline{GH}$, the ratio is less than 1.00 and the image is
        smaller than the pre-image.

    b. When $\overline{EF}$ is longer than $\overline{GH}$, the ratio is greater than 1.00 and the image is
        larger than the pre-image.

    c. When $\overline{EF}$ and $\overline{GH}$ have equal lengths, the ratio is 1.00 and the figures coincide.

Answers for Similar Figures Activity

2. a. $\overline{TI}$, $\overline{IN}$, $\overline{NY}$, $\overline{YT}$,   b. 2.0 (or 0.5)

    c. ∠YTI, ∠TIN, ∠INY, ∠NYT   d. They are equal.

4. **REDIPS**; $m\angle YWE \neq m\angle EDI$ 6. **LAUGH**; $m\angle EIN \neq m\angle HGU$

8. a. 1.5   b. 1.5

    c. $\overline{FT}$ = 4 inches; $\frac{6}{x} = \frac{3}{2}$ d. Answers will vary.

    e. Same measure as 8d; corresponding angles of similar triangles are congruent.

Solution for Mission: Matched Pairs Project

Answers for Transformations Wrap-Up

1. a. C, D   b. B, E   c. F

2. a. reflection   b. rotation   c. rotation

    d. rotation   e. translation

3. a.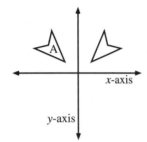

    b.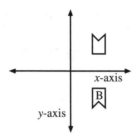

    c.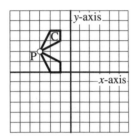

    d.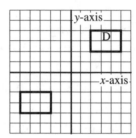

    e.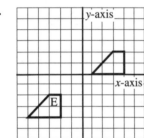

    f.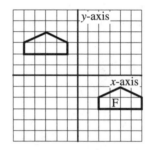

4. **WO**

5. ∠**YTS**

6. **BI**

7. ∠**PEA** or ∠**AEP**

8. 1.2 units

9. 60°

Exploring Translations

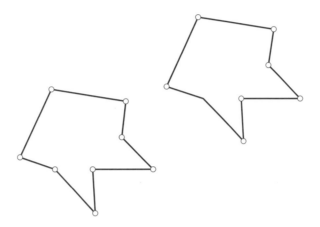

1. Open a new sketch.

2. Construct a polygon (use the **Segment** tool ◺). This figure is your pre-image.

Use Sketchpad to translate your polygon.

3. Select your polygon (use the **Selection Arrow** tool ▸).

4. Go to the Transform menu and choose **Translate.**

5. In the dialog box, choose **By Rectangular Vector.**

6. Enter a Horizontal and a Vertical distance.

7. Click OK. This new figure is your image.

8. Drag any vertex or side of your pre-image. Observe the effects on the image.

9. Go to the Edit menu and choose **Undo** until you see only your original selected pre-image.

10. Repeat steps 4, 5, 6, and 7, entering different values for the Horizontal and Vertical distances. You may want to use some negative values. Observe the results.

11. Drag your figure again and make observations.

12. Based on your observations, define *translation*. Include the relationship between sizes, shapes, and locations of the pre-image and image.

_____

_____

Alternate Method for Translations

13. Go to the Edit menu and choose **Undo** until you see only your original pre-image.

14. Using the **Segment** tool ⟋, construct a short segment in your sketch.

15. Click on the two endpoints of the segment. Make sure only the endpoints are selected, not the segment itself.

16. Go to the Transform menu and choose **Mark Vector.**

17. Select the sides and vertices of your polygon (use the **Selection Arrow** tool ⬆).

18. Go to the Transform menu and choose **Translate.**

19. In the dialog box, choose **Marked.**

20. Click Translate. You should see a new image appear.

21. Drag one of the endpoints of the vector segment. Observe the image as you drag either endpoint of the segment. How does this affect the size, shape, and position of the image?

_____

_____

22. Drag one of the vertices of the pre-image. How does this affect the size, shape, and position of the image?

_____

_____

23. How is the effect of changing the vector different from the effect of changing the pre-image?

_____

_____

24. Compare the two methods you have learned for translating a figure.

_____

_____

_____

Exploring Rotations

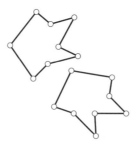

1. Open a new sketch.

2. Construct a polygon (use the **Segment** tool ✏). This figure is your pre-image.

Use Sketchpad to rotate your polygon.

3. Construct a point near your polygon (use the **Point** tool ⊡).

4. While this point is selected, go to the Transform menu and choose **Mark Center.**

5. Select the sides and vertices of your polygon (use the **Selection Arrow** tool ⬉).

6. Go to the Transform menu and choose **Rotate.**

7. Enter an angle measure in the dialog box.

8. Click Rotate. This new figure is your image.

9. Drag any vertex or side of your pre-image. Observe the effects on the image.

10. Go to the Edit menu and choose **Undo** until you see only your original pre-image.

11. Repeat steps 5, 6, 7, and 8, entering different values for the angle of rotation. You may want to use some negative values. Observe the results.

12. Drag your figure again and make observations.

13. Based on your observations, define *rotation*. Include the relationship between sizes, shapes, and locations of the pre-image and image.

_____

_____

14. Drag the point you marked as your center of rotation. Make observations. Use your observations to define a *center of rotation.*

_____

_____

_____

Alternate Method for Rotations

15. Go to the Edit menu and choose **Undo** until you see only your original pre-image.

16. Construct an angle in your sketch (use the **Segment** tool ▱).

17. Click on the points that define the angle, in clockwise or counterclockwise order. Make sure the vertex of the angle is the second point you choose (use the **Selection Arrow** tool ▣).

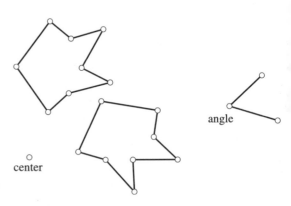

center

angle

18. Go to the Transform menu and choose **Mark Angle.**

19. Select the sides and vertices of your polygon (use the **Selection Arrow** tool ▣).

20. Go to the Transform menu and choose **Rotate.**

21. Click Rotate in the dialog box. You should see a new image appear.

22. Drag one of the points defining your angle of rotation. Observe the image as you drag. How does this affect the size, shape, and position of the image?

_____

_____

23. Drag one of the vertices of the pre-image. How does this affect the size, shape, and position of the image?

_____

_____

24. How is the effect of changing the angle of rotation different from the effect of changing the pre-image?

_____

_____

25. Compare the two methods you have learned for rotating a figure.

_____

_____

_____

Geometry Activities for Middle School Students with The Geometer's Sketchpad
©2004 by Key Curriculum Press

Exploring Transformations with Freehand Tools

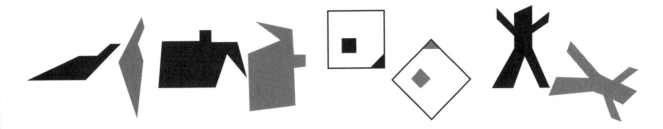

Use the freehand tools with the Transform menu in Sketchpad to explore transformations.

1. Open the sketch **Moves.gsp** and go to the page "Moves 1."

2. Use reflections, rotations, and/or translations to move the darker shaded figure on top of the other figure.

3. Go to the page "Moves 2."

4. Use reflections, rotations, and/or translations to move the darker shaded figure on top of the other figure.

5. Go to the page "Moves 3."

6. Use reflections, rotations, and/or translations to move the darker shaded figure on top of the other figure.

7. Go to the page "Moves 4."

8. Use reflections, rotations, and/or translations to move the darker shaded figure on top of the other figure. Use the space below to briefly describe the transformations you used to make this happen.

_____

_____

_____

On Your Own: Reopen one of the sketches in this activity. Try to use a different transformation or set of transformations than you did the first time to move the darker shaded figure onto the lighter figure.

Transformations on the Coordinate Grid

Use Sketchpad to explore transformations on the coordinate grid.

1. Open the sketch **Grids.gsp** and go to the page "Grids 1."

2. Imagine the image of polygon **MYTHRONE** after it is reflected over the *y*-axis. On the grid at left below, sketch the image as you think it will appear.

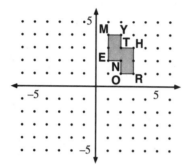
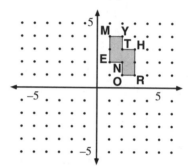

3. Reflect **MYTHRONE** over the *y*-axis.
   a. Mark the *y*-axis as a mirror.
   b. Select the vertices, sides, and polygon interior of **MYTHRONE**.
   c. Go to the Transform menu and choose **Reflect.**

4. On the grid at right above, sketch the image of **MYTHRONE** after reflection. Give the coordinates of **M′** and **R′**. **M′**(_____) **R′**(_____)

5. Go to the Edit menu and choose **Undo** until your reflection no longer appears.

6. Imagine the image of **MYTHRONE** after it is rotated 90° clockwise about the origin. On the grid at left below, sketch the image as you think it will appear.

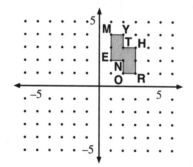
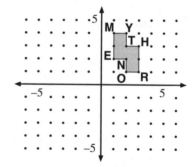

7. Rotate **MYTHRONE** −90° about the origin.
   a. Mark the origin as a center.
   b. Select the vertices, sides, and polygon interior of **MYTHRONE**.
   c. Go to the Transform menu and choose **Rotate.** Enter −90 in the dialog box.

8. On the grid at right in step 6, sketch the image of **MYTHRONE** after the rotation. Give the coordinates of **M′** and **R′**. **M′**(_____) **R′**(_____)

9. Go to the Edit menu and choose **Undo** until your rotation no longer appears.

10. Imagine the image of **MYTHRONE** after it is translated by ⟨−5, 1⟩. (Remember that ⟨−5, 1⟩ means to move each point 5 units to the left and 1 unit up.) On the grid to the left below, sketch the image as you think it will appear.

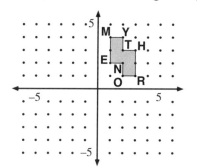 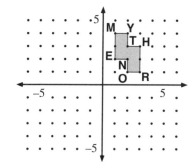

11. Translate **MYTHRONE** by ⟨−5, 1⟩.
    a. Select the vertices, sides, and polygon interior of **MYTHRONE**.
    b. Go to the Transform menu and choose **Translate.**
    c. Be sure **By Rectangular Vector** is chosen in the dialog box.
    d. Enter −5 as the Horizontal value and 1 as the Vertical value, and click Translate.

12. On the grid to the right above, sketch the image of **MYTHRONE** after the translation. Give the coordinates of **M′** and **R′**. **M′**(_____) **R′**(_____)

13. Go to the page "Grids 2."

14. Imagine the image of **TADPOL** after it is reflected over the x-axis. On the grid at left below, sketch the image as you think it will appear.

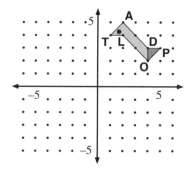 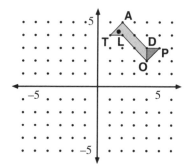

15. Reflect **TADPOL** over the *x*-axis.

    a. Mark the *x*-axis as a mirror.

    b. Select the vertices, sides, and polygon interiors of **TADPOL**.

    c. Choose **Reflect** from the Transform menu and reflect the pre-image.

16. On the grid at right in step 14, sketch the image of **TADPOL** after the reflection. Give the coordinates of **A′** and **P′**. **A′**(_____) **P′**(_____)

17. Go to the Edit menu and choose **Undo** until your reflection no longer appears.

18. Imagine the image of **TADPOL** after it is rotated 90° counterclockwise about the origin. On the grid at left below, sketch the image as you think it will appear.

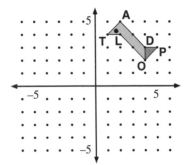 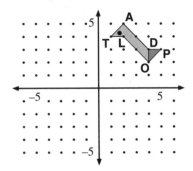

19. Rotate **TADPOL** 90° about the origin.

    a. Mark the origin as a center.

    b. Select the vertices, sides, and polygon interiors of **TADPOL**.

    c. Choose **Rotate** from the Transform menu, enter 90 in the dialog box, and click Rotate.

20. On the grid at right above, sketch the image of **TADPOL** after the rotation. Give the coordinates of **A′** and **P′**. **A′**(_____) **P′**(_____)

21. Go to the Edit menu and choose **Undo** until your rotation no longer appears.

22. Imagine the image of **TADPOL** after it is translated by ⟨–3, –4⟩. On the grid at left below, sketch the image as you think it will appear.

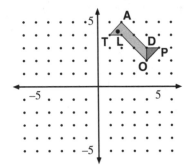 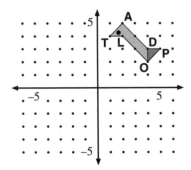

23. Translate **TADPOL** by $\langle -3, -4 \rangle$.

    a. Select the vertices, sides, and polygon interiors of **TADPOL**.

    b. Choose **Translate** from the Transform menu.

    c. Be sure **By Rectangular Vector** is chosen in the dialog box.

    d. Enter −3 as the Horizontal value and −4 as the Vertical value, and click Translate.

24. On the grid at right in step 22, sketch the image of **TADPOL** after the translation.

    Give the coordinates of **A´** and **P´**. **A´**(_____) **P´**(_____)

On Your Own: Reopen the sketch **Grids.gsp** and go to the "Grids 1" page. Perform a transformation somewhat different from any in this activity. Then perform a transformation on the image you just created. Print out the sketch. Now hide the first image and print out the sketch again. Compare second printouts with your partner to see whether each of you can guess the two transformations used by the other to create the final image. Turn in all printouts.

Glide Reflections

A *glide reflection* is a combination of two transformations. Use Sketchpad to explore glide reflections.

1. Open a new sketch.

2. Use the **Segment** tool ◱ to draw a polygon.

3. Construct the polygon interior.

4. Construct a segment and a point on the segment. The points are labeled **A**, **B**, and **C** in the diagram at right for easy identification.

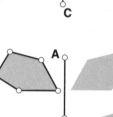

5. Double-click on the segment to mark it as a mirror.

6. Select the polygon interior, go to the Transform menu, and choose **Reflect.**

7. Use the **Selection Arrow** tool ▮ to select point **A** and then point **B**.

8. Go to the Transform menu and choose **Mark Vector.**

9. Select the image (the reflected polygon). Go to the Transform menu, choose **Translate,** and choose **Marked** in the dialog box. Click Translate.

10. Drag your original figure or point **B** and notice how the images are affected. What two transformations are used in a glide reflection? _____ / _____

On Your Own: Open a new sketch and create your own custom transformation. Make two copies of your sketch. One copy should show all stages. The other copy should have all objects hidden except your original polygon and the final image.

Geometry Activities for Middle School Students with The Geometer's Sketchpad
©2004 by Key Curriculum Press

Dilations

A *dilation* is a transformation that shrinks or enlarges a figure. (Unlike other transformations, the *image* is not necessarily the same size as the *pre-image*.) Use Sketchpad to investigate dilations.

1. Open the sketch **Dilations.gsp** and go to the page "Dilations 1."

2. Dilate △**ABC** by using a scale factor.

   a. Using the **Selection Arrow** tool ▶, click on point **D**. Go to the Transform menu and choose **Mark Center.**

   b. Use a selection marquee to select △**ABC**. Go to the Transform menu and choose **Dilate.**

   c. When the Dilate dialog box appears, for Scale Factor enter 3 in the top (numerator) box and 4 in the bottom (denominator) box. Click Dilate.

   You should see another, smaller triangle appear to the right of the original triangle.

3. Find the ratio of a pair of corresponding sides in the two triangles.

   a. Click on a side of your image (the new triangle). Then click on the corresponding side of the pre-image (the original triangle).

   b. Go to the Measure menu and choose **Ratio.**

   What ratio appears on your screen for this pair of corresponding sides? _____

4. Follow the directions in step 3 to find the ratio for each pair of corresponding sides of your triangles.

   What is the relationship between the *length of new* and the *length of old* for every pair of corresponding sides? _____

5. Measure an angle of the pre-image and a corresponding angle of the image.
   How do the measures compare? _____

6. Find the measures of each pair of corresponding angles in the triangles.

   a. How do the measures of pairs of corresponding angles compare? _____

   _____

   b. What is the ratio of the measures of any pair of corresponding angles? _____

7. Undo your dilation. Dilate the original figure by the ratio 5 : 4 (5 in the top (numerator) box and 4 in the bottom (denominator) box.)

   Answer the following questions. (Verify each by measuring, if needed.)

   a. What is the ratio *length of new : length of old* for each pair of corresponding sides? _____

   b. What is the ratio *measure of new : measure of old* for each pair of corresponding angles? _____

8. Explain in your own words how the corresponding sides and angles of the pre-image and image will relate if you create the image by a fixed ratio of 2 : 3 (2 as Numerator and 3 as Denominator.)

   _____

   _____

9. Go to the page "Dilations 2."

10. Dilate quadrilateral **ABCD** by a marked ratio.

    a. Using the **Selection Arrow** tool ⌷ , click on point **P**. Go to the Transform menu and choose **Mark Center.**

    b. Click on $\overline{EF}$ and then on $\overline{GH}$. Go to the Transform menu and choose **Mark Segment Ratio.**

    c. Use a selection marquee to select quadrilateral **ABCD**. Go to the Transform menu and choose **Dilate.**

    d. When the Dilate dialog box appears, make sure **By Marked Ratio** is chosen. Then click Dilate. You should see another, smaller quadrilateral appear to the right of the original quadrilateral.

11. Click on $\overline{EF}$ and then on $\overline{GH}$. Go to the Measure menu and choose **Ratio.**

12. Click on a side of your image (the new quadrilateral). Then click on the corresponding side of the pre-image (the original quadrilateral). Go to the Measure menu and choose **Ratio.**

    How does the ratio of the side lengths compare to the marked ratio? _____

    _____

13. Repeat step 12 to find the ratio for each pair of corresponding sides of your quadrilaterals.

    Is the ratio *length of new : length of old* the same for every pair of corresponding sides? _____

14. Measure an angle of the pre-image and a corresponding angle of the image. How do the measures compare? _____

15. Find the measures of each pair of corresponding angles in the quadrilaterals. Answer the following questions.

    a. How do the measures of pairs of corresponding angles compare?

    _____

    b. What is the ratio of the measures of any pair of corresponding angles?

    _____

    c. Are these results consistent with the results you got using the first method for dilating? _____ Explain why or why not. _____

    _____

16. Drag one or more endpoints of $\overline{EF}$ and $\overline{GH}$. Answer the following questions.

    a. What is the effect on the figures and the ratio when $\overline{EF}$ is shorter than $\overline{GH}$?

    _____

    b. What is the effect on the figures and the ratio when $\overline{EF}$ is longer than $\overline{GH}$?

    _____

    c. What is the effect on the figures and the ratio when $\overline{EF}$ is equal in length to $\overline{GH}$?

    _____

On Your Own: Open a new sketch. Draw an angle and a circle. Dilate each, using both methods you have learned. Create a label for each pair showing the ratio of corresponding measures. For the angles, compare their measures in degrees. For the circles, compare the measures of their radii. Put your name on the sketch and print out a copy to turn in.

Similar Figures

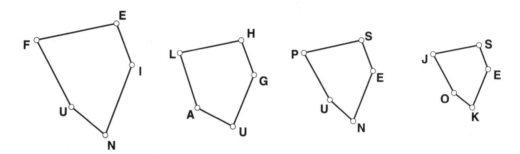

Use Sketchpad to explore similar polygons.

1. Open the sketch **Similarity.gsp** ond go to the page "Similarity 1."

2. Quadrilateral **TINY** is similar to quadrilateral **LARG**. With this information in mind, answer each question below.

   a. List the pairs of corresponding sides in quadrilateral **TINY** for each side of quadrilateral **LARG**.

      $\overline{LA}$ _____ , $\overline{AR}$ _____ , $\overline{RG}$ _____ , $\overline{GL}$ _____

   b. What is the ratio of the lengths of each pair of corresponding sides in the quadrilaterals? _____

   c. List the pairs of corresponding angles in **TINY** for each angle in **LARG**.

      $\angle$**GLA** _____ , $\angle$**LAR** _____ , $\angle$**ARG** _____ , $\angle$**RGL** _____

   d. What is the relationship of the measures of each pair of corresponding angles in the quadrilaterals? _____

3. Go to the page "Similarity 2."

4. Hexagon **FLYWEB** is similar to two of the other hexagons shown, but not to the third. Use the ratios of corresponding sides and the measures of corresponding angles to determine which hexagon is *not* similar to **FLYWEB**. Which hexagon is *not* similar to the others? _____ Explain how your measures show that you are correct.

   _____

   _____

   _____

5. Go to the page "Similarity 3."

Geometry Activities for Middle School Students with The Geometer's Sketchpad
©2004 by Key Curriculum Press

6. Pentagon **FUNIE** is similar to two of the other pentagons shown, but not to the third. Use ratios of corresponding sides and measures of corresponding angles to find the pentagon that is *not* similar. Which pentagon is *not* similar to the others? _____ Explain how your measures show that you are correct. _____

_____

_____

7. Go to the page "Similarity 4."

8. Since corresponding sides in similar figures have the same ratio and corresponding angles have the same measure, you can often find the lengths of unknown sides and measures of unknown angles. Triangle **HAN** is similar to triangle **FUT**. With this information in mind, answer each question below.

   a. Find the ratio of $\overline{HN} : \overline{FT}$. What is this ratio? _____

   b. What is the ratio of the lengths of any two corresponding sides? _____

   c. If $\overline{HN}$ is 6 inches long, how long is $\overline{FT}$? (You may use a proportion to solve.)

   _____ How do you know you are correct? _____

   _____

   _____

   d. Measure ∠**AHN**. What is this measure? _____

   e. Without measuring, what is the measure of ∠**UFT**? _____ How do you know you are correct? _____

   _____

   _____

Mission: Matched Pairs

1. Open the sketch **Matched Pairs.gsp.**

   Your mission, should you choose to accept it, is to work together to divide the four-by-four square array shown into two congruent regions that would fill the square. Do this by connecting points to create two separate regions. Mark one solution on each array. You do not have a new solution if the congruent regions are the same as those in another drawing turned in a different direction.

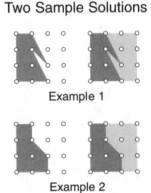

Two Sample Solutions

Example 1

Example 2

2. Check each solution, using the following steps:

   a. Construct the polygon interior on one side of your path.

   b. Select the polygon interior.

   c. Use the appropriate transformation(s) to move the selected polygon so that it fits exactly onto the other half of the array. You may use two reflections or a rotation of 180°. If you choose to rotate, you may double-click on the *Show Centers* button to display the appropriate point to mark as a center for each square.

   See how many different solutions you can find. First work alone. Then compare, check, and combine your findings with those of your partner. Use the grids to show solutions. Put your name on your sketch and print out a copy to hand in.

   You may use the grids below to sketch your solutions.

The Name Game

1. Open a new sketch and use the **Segment** tool 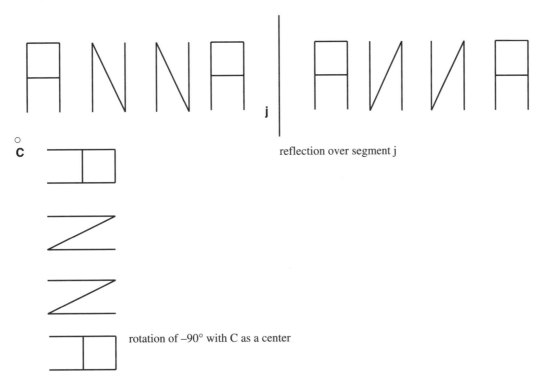 to write your first name or nickname. In the same sketch, create each of the following:

   a. a reflection of your name (show your line of reflection, too)

   b. a rotation of your name (show your marked center, too)

   Note: A rotation may be done by a marked angle (show the angle if you use this method).

   Be sure the images do not overlap!

2. For each transformation, include a caption similar to the ones shown in the example below.

reflection over segment j

rotation of –90° with C as a center

Bonus: You may earn bonus points if you show a translation of your name by using **By Rectangular Vector.** Again, be sure the images do not overlap!

Triangle Buddies

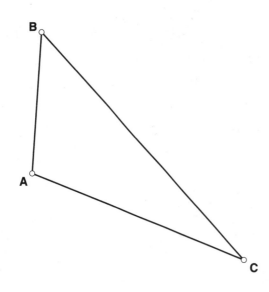

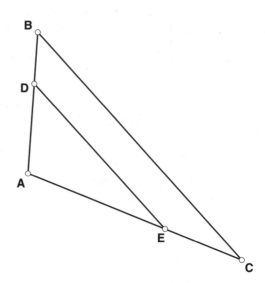

1. Open a new sketch and construct a triangle.

2. Construct a line passing through two sides of the triangle parallel to the third side.

3. Use Sketchpad to see whether the two triangles you now have (△**ABC** and △**ADE** in the example above) are similar. Drag your triangle to see whether your conclusion holds true for any triangle.

4. Make captions showing appropriate measures and ratios and a statement of your conclusions. Put your name on your sketch, print it out, and hand it in.

5. Repeat steps 2 and 3 with a line parallel to a different side of your triangle.

Go, Team, Go

In a *scale drawing,* the ratio of the measures of real objects to those in the drawing is always the same. For example, if the scale for a drawing is 3 cm to 2 m, an object that has a length of 3 cm in the scale drawing has an actual length of 2 m, and the ratio of any two measures of *object in drawing : real object* is 3 : 200.

1. Your group is to measure the basketball court at your school and use Sketchpad to make a scale drawing. Be sure to show the free throw line and lane, the center circles, and all other lines on the court.

2. Put a title, your names, and the scale for your drawing on your sketch. Print out a copy and hand it in.

Basketball Court

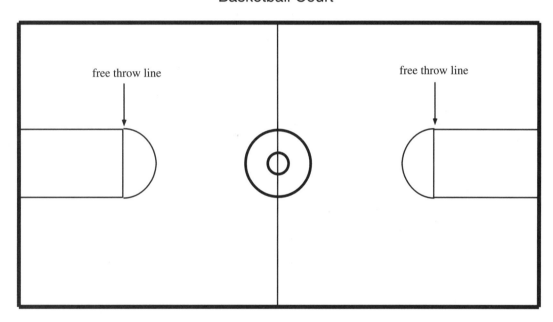

Transform Me!

Use Sketchpad to create a sketch that contains all of the following transformations.

1. Reflection

2. Translation (remember, you can translate by a rectangular vector, by polar vector, or by a marked vector)

3. Rotation (remember, you can rotate by a fixed angle or by a marked angle)

4. Dilation (remember, you can dilate by a fixed ratio or by a marked ratio)

5. Include animation in your sketch. Also, remember to include your name in the sketch.

When Horace and Big George talk, everybody talks!

Big George and Horace

What is the combined circumference of these 6 circles?

radius = 5 cm

6th Period
By Louise L. and Beulah Mae W.

Golden Rectangle Survey

A *golden rectangle* is one in which the ratio of the length (the longer side) to the width creates a shape that supposedly is particularly pleasing. This ratio is referred to as the *golden ratio* and is present when

$$\frac{length}{width} = \frac{(length + width)}{length}$$

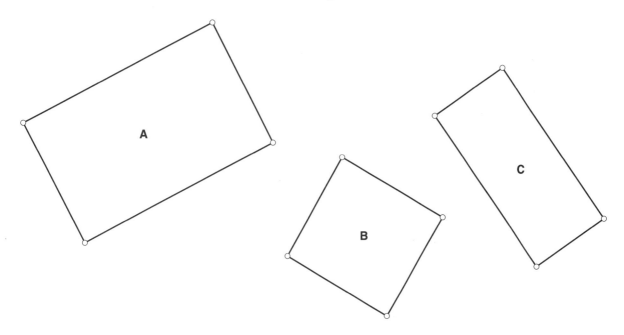

1. Use Sketchpad to construct a golden rectangle.

2. In the same sketch, construct three other rectangles that are *not* golden rectangles. (Do not make the ratio *length : width* close to the golden ratio in your other rectangles.) Print out your sketch.

3. Ask 20 people to tell you which rectangle is the most pleasing. Record their choices.

4. Combine your results with those of your classmates. Did most people choose the golden rectangle as the most pleasing shape?

Think It Over

5. Are all the golden rectangles created by you and your classmates similar? Why or why not? Verify your answer using Sketchpad.

6. If you dilate your golden rectangle, will the new figure also be a golden rectangle? Why or why not? Verify your answer using Sketchpad.

1. Look at designs in wallpaper books or on fabric to find an example of a strip symmetry made using glide reflections. Create a Sketchpad version of the design. Make a poster showing the wallpaper or fabric sample, your sketch, and an explanation of how glide reflections were used to create the design.

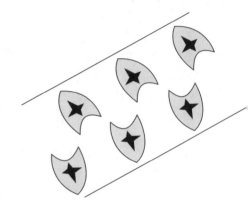

2. Explore the general effects of reflecting figures on the coordinate plane over the *x*- and *y*-axes. Take particular notice of the coordinates of points in the pre-image and image. Can you find any patterns that would allow you to predict the coordinates in the image before you reflect? Make any conjectures you can. Drag the points in your figures to test your ideas.

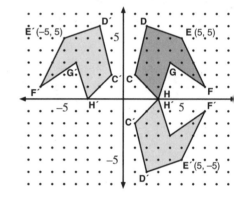

3. Use your knowledge of transformations and similar figures to create several optical illusions. You may want to do some research in your school library or on the Internet for ideas.

Which is greater in length: $\overline{WX}$ or $\overline{YZ}$?

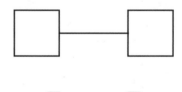

Are the lines connecting the pairs of squares equal in length?

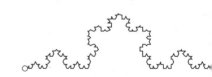

4. Use transformations to create an original fractal. You may want to begin by completing one of the fractals in the Constructions unit (Unit 7) of this book and/or investigating the topic on your own. Be sure you use a Sketchpad script to create the stages of your fractal.

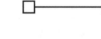

5. Investigate the concept of slope of lines in the graphs of functions on the coordinate plane. Prepare a presentation using sketches you create with Sketchpad to explain slope using translations. For example, translating a point 1 unit horizontally and –2 units vertically several times will produce points on a line with slope –2.

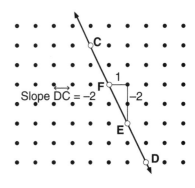

6. Create star polygons with Sketchpad using transformations. Try to create each one using at least two different methods.

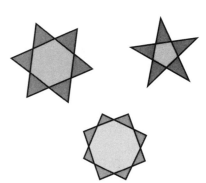

1. Determine which figures are images of figure A under the transformations named in a–c below.

figure A

figure B

figure C

figure D

figure E

figure F

   a. Which figure(s) are images of figure A after *one* reflection? _____

   b. Which figure(s) are images of figure A after a rotation? _____

   c. Which figure(s) are images of figure A after a translation? _____

2. Give one transformation (reflection, rotation, or translation) that will move the pre-image (the first figure listed) onto the image (the second figure listed).

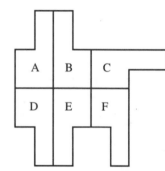

   a. Move figure A onto figure B. _____

   b. Move figure B onto figure C. _____

   c. Move figure B onto figure D. _____

   d. Move figure A onto figure E. _____

   e. Move figure D onto figure F. _____

3. Draw each image that results from the given transformation.

   a.

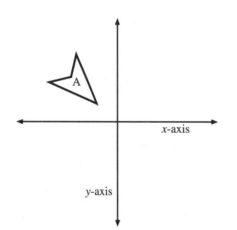

Reflect figure A over the *y*-axis.

   b.

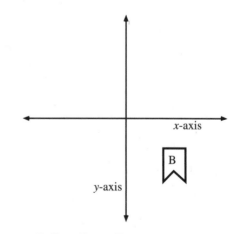

Reflect figure B over the *x*-axis.

Geometry Activities for Middle School Students with The Geometer's Sketchpa
©2004 by Key Curriculum Pres

c.

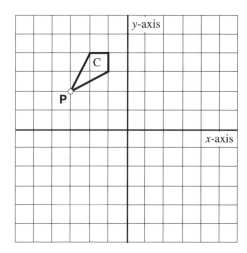

Rotate figure C 90° clockwise around point P.

d.

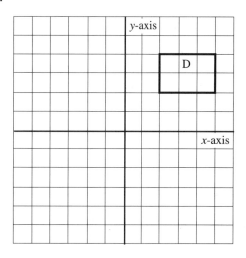

Rotate figure D 180° around the origin.

e.

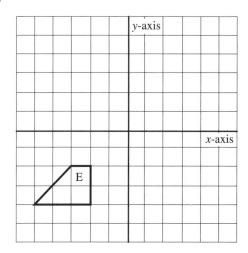

Translate figure E by ⟨6, 4⟩.

f.

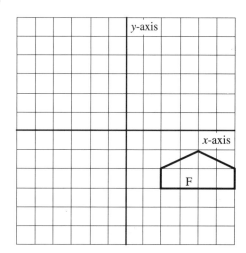

Translate figure F by ⟨–7, 5⟩.

Dilations

Each pair of figures in questions 4–7 is similar. List the corresponding side or angle for the one given.

4.

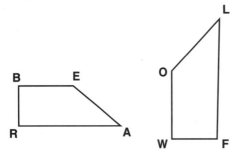

BEAR ~ WOLF

$\overline{BE}$ corresponds to _____ .

5.

PIG ~ STY

∠**PIG** corresponds to _____ .

6.

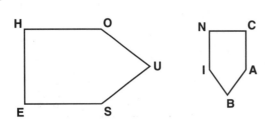

HOUSE ~ CABIN

$\overline{US}$ corresponds to _____ .

7.

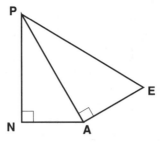

PAN ~ PEA

∠**PAN** corresponds to _____ .

Each pair of figures in questions 8 and 9 is similar. Use your knowledge of similar figures to answer each question.

8.

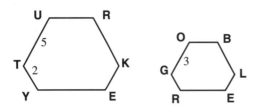

TURKEY ~ GOBLER

How long is $\overline{GR}$? _____

9.

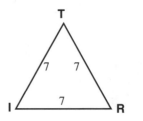

TRI ~ ANG

What is the measure of ∠**ANG**? _____

Geometry Activities for Middle School Students with The Geometer's Sketchpa
©2004 by Key Curriculum Pre

CONSTRUCTIONS

Commentary

This unit provides students with step-by-step instructions that can be used with The Geometer's Sketchpad to produce figures that maintain their essential characteristics. Unlike a drawing, each of the finished products can be dragged and will not "fall apart" or lose its defining properties. In addition, the products are dynamic and allow further exploration, an advantage Euclid and others did not have!

The purpose of these activities is to introduce middle school students to the capabilities of Sketchpad as an alternative to compass and straightedge constructions and to provide experiences that will spark their imaginations to do constructions of their own. We believe they also provide an intuitive base for the constructions and formal proofs the students will encounter later in their mathematics instruction.

Each construction is designed to stand alone; that is, none is dependent upon having done a previous activity, although, of course, related experiences will certainly enhance the benefits. Some of the constructions fit nicely into other units of the book, and for each of these a reference is included in the Teacher Notes of the appropriate unit. For example, using **Constructing an Equilateral Triangle** will be appropriate for some students as they work through the Triangles unit. Other constructions may fit appropriately in two or more places; for example, **Constructing a Golden Rectangle** might be used with some groups during a study of quadrilaterals, whereas for others it might fit best after a study of transformations and similar polygons.

Our intent is that these constructions serve as examples and motivators to middle school students. We love to see their follow-up constructions. Our experience with Sketchpad gives us confidence that middle school students can grasp the concepts of sound constructions and create their own. Give them the tools and a little experience, then step back and get ready for exciting results!

For each construction, the major steps required have been delineated. Detailed instructions are provided for each step and are designated by the compass symbol. Experienced Sketchpad users may not need the detailed instructions included with each step. This format allows such students to proceed at their own pace while providing a foolproof method for less experienced students to have success as well. Don't forget to emphasize the wonderful **Undo** feature of Sketchpad. These activities reinforce that favorite adage of teachers: "Perseverance pays off!"

As they use the software, your students may be eager to use shortcuts with Sketchpad. Some users are skilled enough to use shortcuts almost immediately, whereas others are not sufficiently proficient with either Sketchpad or using a mouse until much later. We certainly believe that any child should be allowed to use any shortcut whenever he or she demonstrates a level of proficiency that minimizes errors. However, it has been our experience with middle school students that it works best to postpone the use of shortcuts with the tools until the students fully understand the steps each shortcut replaces, as discussed in the introduction to this book. For your convenience, we have included a guide to shortcuts with Sketchpad at the end of this unit.

We suggest that you remind students who have minimal Sketchpad experience that to select an object or a figure, one usually clicks on the object with the **Selection Arrow** tool or drags a selection marquee around it.

We believe that including some exposure to constructions in a middle school geometry curriculum is important. Going through such a process adds a dimension to students' mathematical experience that is enriching and, to many, quite motivating as well.

Constructing an Equilateral Triangle

An *equilateral triangle* is a triangle with all three sides the same length. Labels are shown to make the directions clearer, but you don't need labels in your drawing. Whenever needed, use the detailed instructions marked by . *Make sure you have done each step correctly before you go on to the next step.*

Step 1: Open a new sketch and construct a circle with radius **AB**.

  a. Go to the File menu and choose **New Sketch.**

b. Click on the **Compass** tool ⊙ to highlight it. Drag to draw a circle in your sketch.

Step 2: Construct a circle with center **B** and radius **BA**.

  a. Click on the **Selection Arrow** tool ⬆ and click in any blank space to deselect objects.

b. Select point **B** and then point **A**. Go to the Construct menu and choose **Circle By Center+Point.**

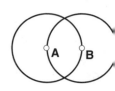

Step 3: Construct intersection point **C**.

  a. Click in any blank space to deselect objects.

b. Select circle **A** and then circle **B** (select the circles, not points **A** and **B**). Go to the Construct menu and choose **Intersections.** Two intersection points will appear. We will use point **C**.

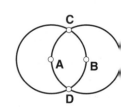

Step 4: Construct $\overline{AB}$, $\overline{AC}$, and $\overline{CB}$.

  a. Click in any blank space to deselect objects.

b. Select points **A**, **B**, and **C**. Go to the Construct menu and choose **Segments.**

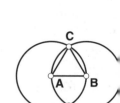

Step 5: Hide the two circles and point **D**.

a. Click in any blank space to deselect objects.

b. Select the two circles and point **D**.

c. Go to the Display menu and choose **Hide Objects.**

Congratulations! You have a new Sketchpad equilateral triangle. Unlike an equilateral triangle that you might draw using only the **Segment** tool ☐, this equilateral triangle stays equilateral when you drag it. See what happens when you drag any of its vertices. Why do you think dragging point **A** or **B** gives a different result than dragging point **C**?

Teach Sketchpad This Construction

1. Use a selection marquee to select your figure. (Make sure all three sides and vertices are selected.)

2. Click on the **Custom** tool ▶: (or ▶▶) and choose **Create New Tool.**

3. Type Equilateral Triangle as the name of your new tool. Click OK.

4. To try out your new custom tool, click and hold on the **Custom** tool ▶: (or ▶▶) until the menu appears. Choose **Equilateral Triangle.**

5. Go to any blank space in your sketch. Click and drag. You should see a new equilateral triangle. If you wish to alter your new triangle, use the **Selection Arrow** tool ↖ and then move the triangle or click in any blank space and drag a vertex to change its size.

6. You can delete your new triangle if you wish before you save your custom tool. All custom tools need to be saved in the **Tool** folder, which is located in the **Sketchpad** folder. Use the **Save As** command under the File menu to save your sketch in this folder. You will need to enter the name Equilateral Triangle again when the Save As dialog box appears.

   Note: Later you can open the sketch containing the custom tool and use your custom **Equilateral Triangle** tool to create an equilateral triangle in any sketch. The new figure will have the same defining characteristics as your original construction.

Follow-Up Construction

Construct an isosceles triangle and create a custom tool for your construction.

Constructing a Parallelogram

A *parallelogram* is a quadrilateral with both pairs of opposite sides parallel. Follow the directions below to construct a parallelogram. Labels are shown to make the directions clearer, but you don't need labels in your sketch. Whenever needed, use the detailed instructions marked by . *Make sure you have done each step correctly before you go on to the next step.*

Step 1: Open a new sketch and construct $\overline{AB}$.

    a. Go to the File menu and choose **New Sketch.**

    b. Using the **Segment** tool , drag to draw a horizontal segment in your sketch.

Step 2: Construct $\overline{AC}$.

    a. Click on point **A** and drag to construct $\overline{AC}$.

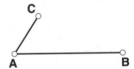

Step 3: Construct a line through point **C**, parallel to $\overline{AB}$.

    a. Click on the **Selection Arrow** tool 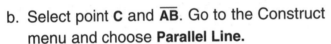 and click in any blank space to deselect objects.

    b. Select point **C** and $\overline{AB}$. Go to the Construct menu and choose **Parallel Line.**

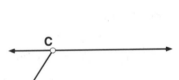

Step 4: Construct a line through point **B** parallel to $\overline{AC}$.

    a. Click in any blank space to deselect objects.

    b. Select point **B** and $\overline{AC}$. Go to the Construct menu and choose **Parallel Line.**

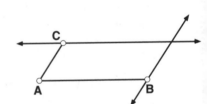

Step 5: Construct intersection point **D**.

    a. Click in any blank space to deselect objects.

    b. Select each of the two lines. Go to the Construct menu and choose **Intersection.**

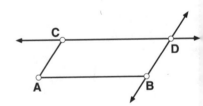

Step 6:   Hide the lines.

a. Click in any blank space to deselect objects.

b. Select $\overleftrightarrow{BD}$ and $\overleftrightarrow{CD}$. Go to the Display menu and choose **Hide Parallel Lines.**

Step 7:   Construct sides $\overline{CD}$ and $\overline{DB}$.

a. Click in any blank space to deselect objects.

b. Select points **C** and **D**. Go to the Construct menu and choose **Segment.**

c. Click in any blank space to deselect objects.

d. Select points **D** and **B**. Go to the Construct menu and choose **Segment.**

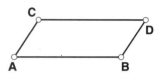

Congratulations! You have a new Sketchpad parallelogram. Unlike a parallelogram that you might draw using only the **Segment** tool 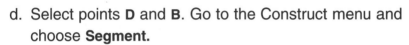, this parallelogram stays a parallelogram when you drag it. See what happens when you drag any of its vertices. Why do you think dragging point **A**, **B**, or **C** gives a different result than dragging point **D**? See whether you can drag a part of your parallelogram so that it appears to be a rectangle, a square, or a rhombus.

Teach Sketchpad This Construction

1. Use a selection marquee to select your figure. (Make sure all four sides and vertices are selected.)

2. Click on the **Custom** tool ▶: (or ▶▶) and choose **Create New Tool.**

3. Type Parallelogram as the name of your new tool. Click OK.

4. To try out your new custom tool, click and hold on the **Custom** tool ▶: (or ▶▶) until the menu appears and choose **Parallelogram.**

5. Go to any blank space in your sketch. Click and drag. You should see a new parallelogram. If you wish to alter your new parallelogram, use the **Selection Arrow** tool ▣ and then move the parallelogram or click in any blank space and drag a vertex to change its appearance.

6. You can delete your new parallelogram if you wish before you save your custom tool. All custom tools need to be saved in the **Tool** folder, which is located in the **Sketchpad** folder. Use the **Save As** command under the File menu to save your sketch in this folder. You will need to enter the name Parallelogram again when the Save As dialog box appears.

Note: Later you can open the sketch containing the custom tool and use your custom **Parallelogram** tool to create a parallelogram in any sketch. The new figure will have the same defining characteristics as your original construction.

Follow-Up Constructions

Construct any two of the figures listed below. Notice the characteristics given in each definition. Be sure your figure keeps those characteristics when dragged and does not fall apart. Make a custom tool for each of your constructions.

A. *Rhombus*—a quadrilateral with both pairs of opposite sides parallel and all side lengths equal.

B. *Rectangle*—a parallelogram with four right angles.

C. *Square*—a rectangle with all sides congruent, or a rhombus with four right angles.

D. *Trapezoid*—a quadrilateral with exactly one pair of parallel sides.

Constructing a Rhombus

A *rhombus* is defined as either a quadrilateral with both pairs of opposite sides parallel and all side lengths equal or as a parallelogram with all sides congruent. Follow the directions below to construct a rhombus. Labels are shown to make the directions clearer, but you don't need labels in your drawing. Whenever needed, use the detailed instructions marked by . *Make sure you have done each step correctly before you go on to the next step.*

Step 1: Open a new sketch and construct a circle.

  a. Go to the File menu and choose **New Sketch.**

b. Click on the **Compass** tool ⊙. Drag in your sketch to draw a circle.

Step 2: Construct radius $\overline{AB}$.

  a. Click on the **Selection Arrow** tool ⬉ and click in any blank space to deselect objects.

b. Select points **A** and **B**, go to the Construct menu, and choose **Segment.**

Step 3: Construct $\overline{AC}$, where **C** is any point on the circle.

a. Click in any blank space to deselect objects.

b. Select the circle (not a point on the circle). Go to the Construct menu and choose **Point On Circle.**

c. Select points **A** and **C**. Go to the Construct menu and choose **Segment.**

Step 4: Construct a line through point **C** parallel to $\overline{AB}$.

  a. Click in any blank space to deselect objects.

b. Select point **C** and $\overline{AB}$. Go to the Construct menu and choose **Parallel Line.**

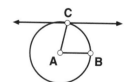

Step 5: Construct a line through point **B**, parallel to $\overline{AC}$.

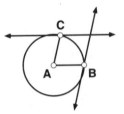

   a. Click in any blank space to deselect objects.

   b. Select point **B** and $\overline{AC}$. Go to the Construct menu and choose **Parallel Line.**

Step 6: Construct intersection point **D**.

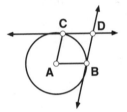

   a. Click in any blank space to deselect objects.

   b. Select each of the two lines. Go to the Construct menu and choose **Intersection.**

Step 7: Hide the circle and $\overleftrightarrow{CD}$ and $\overleftrightarrow{BD}$.

   a. Click in any blank space to deselect objects.

   b. Select the circle (not a point on the circle) and $\overleftrightarrow{CD}$ and $\overleftrightarrow{BD}$. Go to the Display menu and choose **Hide Path Objects.**

Step 8: Construct $\overline{CD}$ and $\overline{BD}$.

   a. Click in any blank space to deselect objects.

   b. Select points **C** and **D**. Go to the Construct menu and choose **Segment.**

   c. Click in any blank space to deselect objects. Select points **B** and **D**. Go to the Construct menu and choose **Segment.**

Congratulations! You have a new Sketchpad rhombus. Unlike a rhombus that you might draw using only the **Segment** tool ▱, this rhombus stays a rhombus when you drag it. See what happens when you drag any of its vertices. Why do you think dragging point **A**, **B**, or **C** gives a different result than dragging point **D**? See whether you can drag a part of your rhombus so that it appears to be a square.

Teach Sketchpad This Construction

1. Use a selection marquee to select your figure. (Make sure all four sides and vertices are selected.)

2. Click on the **Custom** tool ▶: (or ▶▶) and choose **Create New Tool.**

3. Type Rhombus as the name of your new tool. Click OK.

4. To try out your new custom tool, click and hold on the **Custom** tool ▶️ (or ▶▶) until the menu appears, and then choose **Rhombus.**

5. Go to any blank space in your sketch. Click and drag. You should see a new rhombus. If you wish to alter your new rhombus, use the **Selection Arrow** tool ▐↖ and then move the rhombus or click in any blank space and drag a vertex to change its appearance.

6. You can delete your new rhombus if you wish before you save your custom tool. All custom tools need to be saved in the **Tool** folder, which is located in the **Sketchpad** folder. Use the **Save As** command under the File menu to save your sketch in this folder. You will need to enter the name Rhombus again when the Save As dialog box appears.

Note: Later you can open the sketch containing the custom tool and use your custom **Rhombus** tool to create a rhombus in any sketch. The new figure will have the same defining characteristics as your original construction.

Follow-Up Constructions

Construct any two of the figures listed below. Notice the characteristics given in each definition. Be sure your figure keeps those characteristics when dragged and does not fall apart. Make a custom tool for each of your constructions.

A. *Parallelogram*—a quadrilateral with two pairs of parallel sides, or a quadrilateral whose opposite sides are congruent.

B. *Rectangle*—a parallelogram with four right angles.

C. *Square*—a rectangle with all sides congruent, or a rhombus with four right angles.

D. *Trapezoid*—a quadrilateral with exactly one pair of parallel sides.

Constructing a Golden Rectangle

A *golden rectangle* is a rectangle in which the ratio of the length (the longer side) to the width is the *golden ratio.* This ratio exists when

$$\frac{\text{length}}{\text{width}} = \frac{\text{length} + \text{width}}{\text{length}}$$

Follow the directions below to construct a golden rectangle. Labels are shown to make the directions clearer, but you don't need labels in your drawing. Whenever needed, use the detailed instructions marked by ![]. *Make sure you have done each step correctly before you go on to the next step.*

Step 1:   Open a new sketch and construct a square.

    a. Go to the File menu and choose **New Sketch.**

    b. Click on the **Segment** tool ![] and construct $\overline{AB}$.

    c. Use the **Selection Arrow** tool ![] to select point **A**. Go to the Transform menu and choose **Mark Center.**

    d. Select point **B** and $\overline{AB}$. Go to the Transform menu and choose **Rotate.**

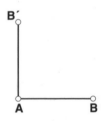

    e. In the dialog box, choose **By Fixed Angle** and enter 90. Click Rotate. Click in any blank space to deselect objects.

    f. Select point **B′**. Go to the Transform menu and choose **Mark Center.**

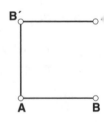

    g. Select point **A** and $\overline{AB'}$. Go to the Transform menu and choose **Rotate.**

    h. In the dialog box, choose **By Fixed Angle** and enter 90. Click Rotate. Click in any blank space to deselect objects.

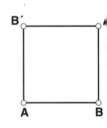

    i. Select points **A′** and **B**. Go to the Construct menu and choose **Segment.**

Step 2:   Construct midpoint **C** on side $\overline{AB}$.

    a. Click in any blank space to deselect objects.

    b. Select $\overline{AB}$. Go to the Construct menu and choose **Midpoint.**

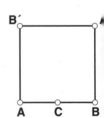

Step 3:   Construct $\overline{CA'}$.

    a. Click in any blank space to deselect objects.

    b. Select point **C** and then point **A'**. Go to the Construct menu and choose **Segment.**

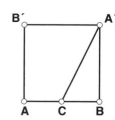

Step 4:   Construct a circle with center **C** and radius $\overline{CA'}$.

    a. Click in any blank space to deselect objects.

    b. Select point **C** and segment $\overline{CA'}$. Go to the Construct menu and choose **Circle By Center+Radius.**

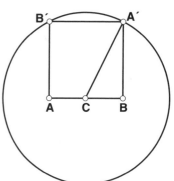

Step 5:   Extend side $\overline{AB}$ to intersect the circle at point **D**.

    a. Click in any blank space to deselect objects.

    b. Using the **Selection Arrow** tool ⬉, select point **A** and then point **B**. Go to the Construct menu and choose **Ray.**

    c. Click in any blank space to deselect objects. Select $\overrightarrow{AB}$ and the circle. Go to the Construct menu and choose **Intersection.**

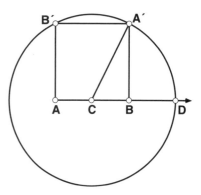

Step 6:   Construct a line perpendicular to $\overrightarrow{AB}$ through **D**.

    a. Click in any blank space to deselect objects.

    b. Select $\overrightarrow{AB}$ and point **D**. Go to the Construct menu and choose **Perpendicular Line.**

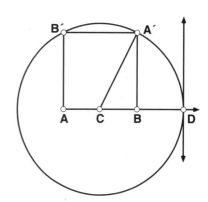

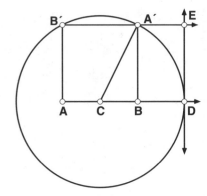

Step 7: Extend $\overline{B'A'}$ to intersect the perpendicular line at point **E**.

a. Click in any blank space to deselect objects.

b. Select point **B'** and then point **A'**. Go to the Construct menu and choose **Ray.**

c. Select $\overrightarrow{B'A'}$ and the perpendicular line. Go to the Construct menu and choose **Intersection.**

Step 8: Hide all unneeded parts to leave rectangle **AB'ED**.

a. Click in any blank space to deselect objects.

b. Select any unwanted points, segments, rays, as well as the circle. Go to the Display menu and choose **Hide Objects.**

step b

c. Click on the **Selection Arrow** tool ⬚. Select points **A**, **B'**, **E**, and **D**, *in that order.* Go to the Construct menu and choose **Segments.**

step c

Step 9: Measure the sides of rectangle **AB'ED** and find the ratio of its length to its width.

a. Go to the Edit menu and choose **Preferences.** Set all Precision settings to hundred thousandths.

b. Click in any blank space to deselect objects.

c. Select sides $\overline{DA}$ and $\overline{ED}$. Go to the Measure menu and choose **Length.**

d. Choose **Calculate** from the Measure menu.

e. Click on the measure of $\overline{DA}$, click on Divide (÷) in the New Calculation dialog box, click on the measure of $\overline{ED}$, and then click OK.

$$\frac{m\,\overline{DA}}{m\,\overline{ED}} = 1.61803$$

New Calculation Dialog Box (Windows)

Geometry Activities for Middle School Students with The Geometer's Sketchpad
©2004 by Key Curriculum Press

Step 10: Find the ratio of (length + width) to length of rectangle **AB´ED**.

   a. Choose **Calculate** from the Measure menu.

   b. Click on Open Parenthesis "(" in the New Calculation dialog box, click on the measure of $\overline{DA}$, click on Plus (+) in the dialog box, click on the measure of $\overline{ED}$, click on Close Parenthesis ")" in the dialog box and then on Divide (÷), click on the measure of $\overline{DA}$, and then click OK to close the dialog box.

Drag point **A**. Compare the two ratios. Do the ratios change as you change the size of your rectangle? _____

Is each rectangle displayed as a golden rectangle? _____

Constructing a Sketchpad Kaleidoscope

Follow the directions below to construct a Sketchpad kaleidoscope. Whenever needed, use the detailed instructions marked by . *Make sure you have done each step correctly before you go on to the next step.*

Step 1:   Open a new sketch and construct a many-sided polygon.

a. Go to the File menu and choose **New Sketch.**

b. Use the **Segment** tool ☑ to construct a polygon with many sides (make it long and somewhat slender).

Step 2:   Construct several polygon interiors within your polygon. Shade them different colors.

a. Click on the **Selection Arrow** tool ☒ and click in any blank space to deselect objects.

b. Select three or four points in clockwise or counterclockwise order.

c. Go to the Construct menu and choose **Polygon Interior** (it may read **Triangle, Quadrilateral,** or other polygon **Interior**).

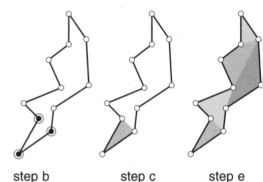

step b   step c   step e

d. While the polygon interior is still selected, go to the Display menu and choose a **Shade** and/or **Color** for your polygon interior.

e. Click in any blank space to deselect objects. Repeat steps b, c, and d until you have several colors or shades of polygon interiors constructed.

Step 3:   Mark the bottom vertex point of your polygon as Center. Hide the points and rotate the polygon 60°.

a. Click in any blank space to deselect objects.

b. Select the bottom vertex point. Go to the Transform menu and choose **Mark Center.**

c. Click on the **Point** tool ⊡. Go to the Edit menu and choose **Select All Points.** Go to the Display menu and choose **Hide Points.**

d. Click on the **Selection Arrow** tool ▲ and drag a selection marquee around all of your polygon to select it. Go to the Transform menu and choose **Rotate.**

e. In the dialog box, choose **By Fixed Angle.** Enter 60 and then click Rotate. (Pick another factor of 360 if you wish.)

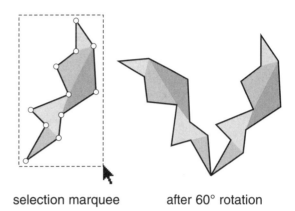

selection marquee   after 60° rotation

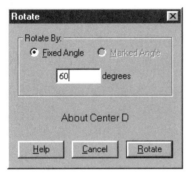

Rotate Dialog Box (Windows)

Step 4:   Continue to rotate the new rotated images until you complete your kaleidoscope.

a. While the rotated image is still selected, go to the Transform menu and rotate this image 60°. Remember to click Rotate.

b. When the newest rotated image appears and while it is still selected, go to the Transform menu and rotate this image 60°. Remember to click Rotate.

c. Repeat this process until you have your complete kaleidoscope constructed.

d. Go to the Display menu and choose **Show All Hidden.** You should see the points on the original arm reappear.

Step 5:   Construct circles with their centers at the center of your kaleidoscope.

a. Click in any blank space to deselect objects.

Note: Make sure when doing steps 5b and c that you release your mouse in a blank space between two arms of your kaleidoscope. You do not want the outside controlling points of your circles to be constructed on any part of your kaleidoscope.

control point

control point

control point

b. Click on the **Compass** tool ⊙. Press on the center point of your kaleidoscope and drag a circle with a radius a little larger than the outside edge of your kaleidoscope.

c. Using the **Compass** tool ⊙, construct a circle with its center at the center of your kaleidoscope, but this time let the radius be about half the radius of your kaleidoscope. Repeat for a circle about one-third the radius of your kaleidoscope.

Step 6: Animate points of your kaleidoscope on the three circles.

a. Click on the **Selection Arrow** tool ↖ and click in any blank space to deselect objects.

b. Select one point on the original polygon near the outside circle and select the outside circle (do not click on one of the control points of the circle). Go to the Edit menu and choose **Merge Point to Circle.** You should see the point travel slowly to the circle.

c. Click in any blank space to deselect objects. Select another point on the original polygon near the middle circle and select the middle circle (do not click on one of the control points of the circle). Go to the Edit menu and choose **Merge Point to Circle.** You should see the point travel slowly to the circle.

Geometry Activities for Middle School Students with The Geometer's Sketchp ©2004 by Key Curriculum Pre

d. Repeat this process to merge a point from the original polygon to the outside circle, then merge a point to the middle circle, and finally merge a point to the smallest circle.

e. Click in any blank space to deselect objects. Select the three points that you merged to the three circles. Go to the Edit menu, choose **Action Buttons,** and choose **Animation** from the submenu. Click OK in the Animate dialog box.

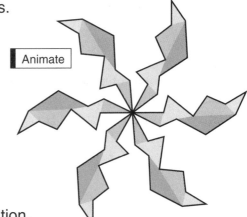

Animate

f. When the Animation button appears, click on it to start the animation. Watch your kaleidoscope turn!

g. Click on the button again to stop the animation. Then click in any blank space to deselect objects.

h. To hide all the points, click on the **Point** tool ⊡. Go to the Edit menu and choose **Select All Points.** Go to the Display menu and choose **Hide Points.**

i. To hide all circles, click on the **Compass** tool ⊙. Go to the Edit menu and choose **Select All Circles.** Go to the Display menu and choose **Hide Circles.**

Constructing a Pantograph

A *pantograph* is a simple mechanical device that uses two pens to draw one figure similar to another on a smaller or larger scale. Christoph Scheiner is given credit for its invention in 1630, but it is possible that it has been around for thousands of years. It has been adapted for many purposes by painters, carvers, sculptors, engravers, and shipbuilders, among others. In this activity, you will use Sketchpad to model a pantograph with your computer. Whenever needed, use the detailed instructions marked by ⚲. Displaying the labels for points may be helpful in this construction. You can choose **Preferences** from the Edit menu, click on the Text tab, and select the **Show Labels Automatically For All New Points** check box, or you can use the **Text** tool A to click on the points to show the labels as you go. *Make sure you have done each step correctly before you go on to the next step.*

Step 1:   Open a new sketch and construct $\overline{AB}$.

a. Go to the File menu and choose **New Sketch.**

b. Click on the **Segment** tool ⧄. Construct a segment, $\overline{AB}$, in your sketch. Segment **AB** is not part of the pantograph but is a control segment that will make your pantograph adjustable.

Step 2:   Construct $\overrightarrow{CD}$.

a. Press and hold down the mouse button on the **Segment** tool ⧄. Drag to the right and click on the **Ray** tool ⬈ to highlight it.

b. Construct a ray similar to the one at right.

Step 3:   Construct circles with centers **C** and **D** and radius **AB**.

a. Click on the **Selection Arrow** tool ⬆ and click in any blank space to deselect objects.

b. Select point **C** and $\overline{AB}$. Go to the Construct menu and choose **Circle By Center+Radius.**

c. Click in any blank space to deselect objects. Select point **D** and $\overline{AB}$. Go to the Construct menu and choose **Circle By Center+Radius.**

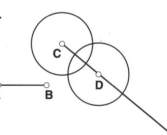

Step 4: Construct $\overrightarrow{CE}$, where **E** is one of the intersection points of these circles, as shown.

   a. Using the **Selection Arrow** tool [↖], click on the top intersection point of the two circles. You should see a point appear there. Use the **Text** tool [A] to label it **E** if needed.

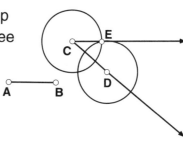

   b. Using the **Selection Arrow** tool [↖], click in any blank space to deselect objects. Select point **C** and then point **E**. Go to the Construct menu and choose **Ray.**

Step 5: Construct $\overline{CE}$ and $\overline{DE}$.

   a. Click in any blank space to deselect objects. Click on point **C** and then on point **E**. Go to the Construct menu and choose **Segment.** (The segment you just constructed overlaps the ray.)

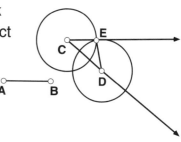

   b. Click in any blank space to deselect objects. Click on point **E** and then on point **D**. Go to the Construct menu and choose **Segment.**

Step 6: Construct $\overline{EF}$, where **F** is any point past **E** on $\overrightarrow{CE}$.

   a. Click in any blank space to deselect objects. Select $\overrightarrow{CE}$ (click to the right of point **E**). Go to the Construct menu and choose **Point On Ray.** Drag point **F** past point **E** if necessary.

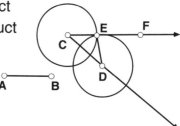

   b. Click on point **E** and then on point **F**. Go to the Construct menu and choose **Segment.**

Step 7: Construct a line through point **F** parallel to $\overline{DE}$ and then construct point **G** where the new line and $\overrightarrow{CD}$ intersect.

a. Click in any blank space to deselect objects. Click on point **F** and then on $\overline{DE}$.

b. Go to the Construct menu and choose **Parallel Line.**

c. Click on this new line and $\overrightarrow{CD}$. Go to the Construct menu and choose **Intersection** to construct point **G**.

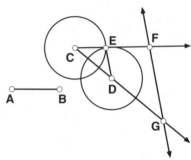

Step 8: Construct a line through point **D** parallel to $\overline{EF}$.

a. Click in any blank space to deselect objects. Click on point **D** and then on $\overline{EF}$.

b. Go to the Construct menu and choose **Parallel Line.**

c. Click on the new parallel line and line **FG**. Go to the Construct menu and choose **Intersection** to construct point **H**.

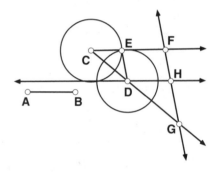

Step 9: Construct $\overline{DH}$, where point **H** is the intersection of the lines constructed in steps 7 and 8.

a. Click in any blank space to deselect objects. Click on point **D** and then click on point **H**.

b. Go to the Construct menu and choose **Segment.**

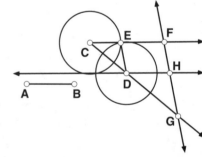

Step 10: Construct $\overline{FG}$.

a. Click in any blank space to deselect objects. Click on point **F** and then on point **G**.

b. Go to the Construct menu and choose **Segment.**

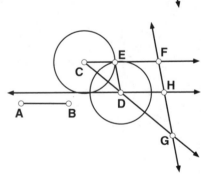

Step 11: Hide the circles, lines, and rays so that your pantograph consists only of segments.

   a. Click in any blank space to deselect objects. Click on the circles, lines, and rays you want to hide.

   b. Go to the Display menu and choose **Hide Path Objects.**

   c. Repeat step b if you missed any objects. Your sketch should look similar to the one at right.

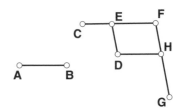

Step 12: Trace points **D** and **G** and drag point **D** to write something.

   a. Click in any blank space to deselect objects. Select points **D** and **G**.

   b. Go to the Display menu and choose **Trace Points.** Click in any blank space to deselect objects. Go to the Edit menu, choose **Preferences,** and click on the Color tab. Make sure **Fade Traces Over Time** is not selected in the dialog box. Click OK.

   c. Select point **D** and slowly drag. Try writing your name with your pantograph.

   d. Go to the Display menu and choose **Erase Traces.**

   e. Change the length of $\overline{AB}$ and try writing your name again. How does this affect the tracing by point **G**?

   f. Go to the Display menu and choose **Erase Traces.**

   g. Change the position of point **F**. How does this affect the tracing by point **G**?

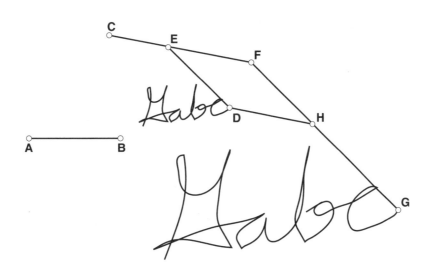

Constructing a Box with Two-Point Perspective

Perspective is a way of drawing three-dimensional objects in two dimensions—on a piece of paper or a computer screen, for example—so that they appear true-to-life. Objects that are farther away appear smaller. Perspective drawings take advantage of this principle to make flat drawings appear to have depth. Follow the directions below to draw a box with two-point perspective. Labels are shown to make the directions clearer, but you don't need labels in your drawing. Whenever needed, use the detailed instructions marked by . *Make sure you have done each step correctly before you go on to the next step.*

Step 1: Open a new sketch.

 a. Go to the File menu and choose **New Sketch.**

Step 2: Draw a long horizontal segment, $\overline{AB}$.

a. Click on the **Segment** tool ▱.

b. Click and drag to draw a segment in your sketch. (If you hold down the Shift key while you drag, it will be easier to make your segment horizontal.)

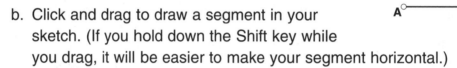

Note: This will be your horizon line, and its endpoints will be the vanishing points of your perspective box.

Step 3: Draw a short, vertical segment, $\overline{CD}$, below your horizon line.

 a. Click and drag with the **Segment** tool ▱ to draw a vertical segment below $\overline{AB}$.

Note: This will be the front edge of your box.

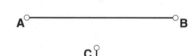

Step 4: Construct $\overline{CA}$, $\overline{DA}$, $\overline{CB}$, and $\overline{DB}$.

 a. Click on the **Selection Arrow** tool ▱ and click in any blank space to deselect objects.

b. Select point **C** and then point **A**.

c. Go to the Construct menu and choose **Segment**.

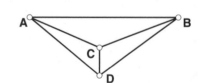

d. Click in any blank space to deselect objects. Select point **D** and then point **A**.

---

e. Go to the Construct menu and choose **Segment.**

f. Click in any blank space to deselect objects. Select point **C** and then point **B**.

g. Go to the Construct menu and choose **Segment.**

h. Click in any blank space to deselect objects. Select point **D** and then point **B**.

i. Go to the Construct menu and choose **Segment.**

Step 5: Construct point **E** on $\overline{DA}$ and point **F** on $\overline{DB}$.

a. Click in any blank space to deselect objects. Select $\overline{DA}$ and $\overline{DB}$.

b. Go to the Construct menu and choose **Points On Segments.**

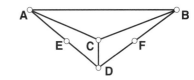

c. Drag each point to approximately the middle of each segment.

Step 6: Construct lines parallel to $\overline{CD}$ through points **E** and **F**.

a. Click in any blank space to deselect objects. Select $\overline{CD}$ and points **E** and **F**.

b. Go to the Construct menu and choose **Parallel Lines.**

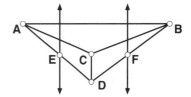

Step 7: Construct the intersection points **G** and **H**.

a. Click in any blank space to deselect objects. Select the parallel line on the left and $\overline{AC}$.

b. Go to the Construct menu and choose **Intersection.**

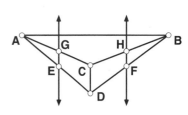

c. Construct point **H** on the parallel line on the right in the same way.

Step 8: Construct $\overline{GB}$ and $\overline{HA}$.

a. Click in any blank space to deselect objects. Select point **G** and then point **B**.

b. Go to the Construct menu and choose **Segment**.

c. Construct $\overline{HA}$ in the same way.

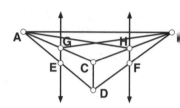

Step 9: Construct point **J** at the intersection of $\overline{GB}$ and $\overline{HA}$.

a. Click in any blank space to deselect objects. Select $\overline{GB}$ and then $\overline{HA}$.

b. Go to the Construct menu and choose **Intersection.**

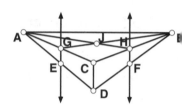

Step 10: Construct $\overline{GJ}$, $\overline{JH}$, $\overline{HF}$, $\overline{FD}$, $\overline{DE}$, $\overline{EG}$, $\overline{GC}$, and $\overline{CH}$.

Note: These segments are the remaining edges of your box. Each overlaps the larger segment or line it is a part of.

a. Click in any blank space to deselect objects. Select point **G** and then point **J**.

b. Go to the Construct menu and choose **Segment.**

c. Construct $\overline{JH}$, $\overline{HF}$, $\overline{FD}$, $\overline{DE}$, $\overline{EG}$, $\overline{GC}$, and $\overline{CH}$ in the same way.

Step 11: Hide all lines and segments that are not part of your box.

a. Click in any blank space to deselect objects. Click outside your box on the part of the line or segment you want to hide.

b. Go to the Display menu and choose **Hide Straight Objects.**

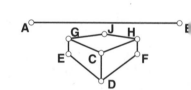

Step 12: Move various parts of your box (you can always undo) until you find the view you like best.

Geometry Activities for Middle School Students with The Geometer's Sketchpad
©2004 by Key Curriculum Press

Extension: If you moved the front edge of your box above your horizontal segment, $\overline{AB}$, you should have noticed that your box has no bottom. Use the following steps to create the missing faces and bottom.

Step 13: Select $\overline{AB}$ and drag it below your box.

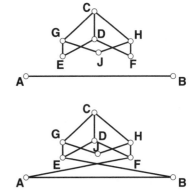

Step 14: Construct $\overline{EB}$ and $\overline{FA}$.

    a. Click in any blank space to deselect objects. Select point **E** and then point **B**.

    b. Go to the Construct menu and choose **Segment.**

    c. Construct $\overline{FA}$ in the same way.

Step 15: Construct point **K** and $\overline{KJ}$.

    a. Click in any blank space to deselect objects. Select $\overline{EB}$ and $\overline{FA}$.

    b. Go to the Construct menu and choose **Intersection.**

    c. Click in any blank space to deselect objects. Select points **J** and **K**.

    d. Go to the Construct menu and choose **Segment.**

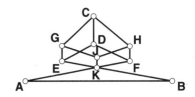

Step 16: Construct $\overline{EK}$ and $\overline{FK}$.

    a. Click in any blank space to deselect objects. Select point **E** and then point **K**.

    b. Go to the Construct menu and choose **Segment.**

    c. Construct $\overline{FK}$ in the same way.

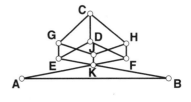

Step 17: Hide unwanted points and segments.

    a. Click in any blank space to deselect objects. Select points and segments you want to hide.

    b. Go to the Display menu and choose **Hide Objects.**

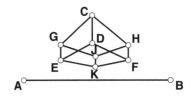

You have a *complete* box with two-point perspective!

Constructing Tessellations by Translations

Follow the directions below to produce a tessellation by translations. You may want to label the points we have labeled in the instructions to more clearly identify the needed points for marking the vectors. Use the **Text** tool to click on the points you wish to label. Whenever needed, use the detailed instructions marked by . *Make sure you have done each step correctly before you go on to the next step.*

Step 1:   Open a new sketch. Construct two adjacent sides of a fractured parallelogram.

    a. Go to the File menu and choose **New Sketch.**

    b. Click on the **Segment** tool and use it to draw a vertical fractured side for your fractured parallelogram (similar to the one from **A** to **B** shown at right). Use the **Text** tool to label points when needed.

    c. Using the **Selection Arrow** tool , click in any blank space to deselect objects.

    d. Using the **Segment** tool , start at point **A** and draw a fractured horizontal side similar to the one shown at right from **A** to **C**.

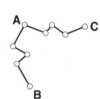

Step 2:   Translate one side of the fractured parallelogram.

    a. Click on the **Selection Arrow** tool . Click in any blank space to deselect objects. Select point **A** and then point **B**.

    b. Go to the Transform menu and choose **Mark Vector.**

    c. Click in any blank space to deselect objects.

    d. Select all points and segments along the fractured side from point **A** to point **C**.

    e. Go to the Transform menu and choose **Translate.** In the dialog box, choose **Marked.** Then click Translate. Your figure should look similar to the one shown at right.

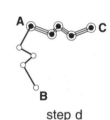

step d

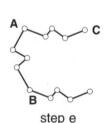

step e

Step 3: Use a translation to complete the fractured parallelogram.

a. Click in any blank space to deselect objects. Select point **A** and then point **C**. Go to the Transform menu and choose **Mark Vector.**

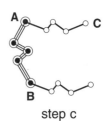

step c

b. Click in any blank space to deselect objects.

c. Select all points and segments along the fractured side from point **A** to point **B**.

d. Go to the Transform menu and choose **Translate.** In the dialog box, choose **Marked.** Then click Translate. Your figure should look similar to the one shown at right.

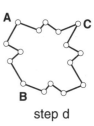

step d

Step 4: Translate your fractured parallelogram to tessellate the plane.

a. Use a selection marquee to select your figure.

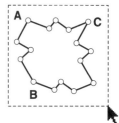

b. Go to the Transform menu and choose **Translate.** Choose **Marked.** Then click Translate. Your figure should look similar to the one shown.

step a

c. While the new figure is selected, repeat step b so that you have three figures in a row.

d. Click in any blank space to deselect objects.

e. Select point **A** and then point **B**.

f. Go to the Transform menu and choose **Mark Vector.**

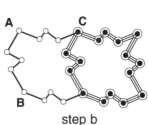

g. Use a selection marquee to select your entire figure.

step b

h. Go to the Transform menu and choose **Translate.** Choose **Marked** in the dialog box. Then click Translate.

i. While the new row is selected, repeat step h to produce a figure similar to the one shown at right.

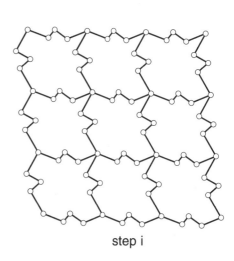

j. Drag a point in one of your fractured parallelograms to see what happens. Continue to drag until you have a shape you like.

step i

k. You may want to construct polygon interiors and shade them to give some contrast to your tessellation. (You can construct just one polygon interior and translate it again and again to fill all the polygons in the tessellation.)

Remember: To construct a polygon interior, select the vertices in clockwise or counterclockwise order, go to the Construct menu, and choose **Polygon Interior.** To change the color of a polygon interior, click on it to select it, go to the Display menu, and choose **Color.** Pick a color you like.

Constructing a Binary Tree Fractal

You will use Sketchpad to create the first stages of a binary tree fractal. Follow the directions below. Labels are shown to make the directions clearer, but you don't need labels in your drawing. Whenever needed, use the detailed instructions marked by . *Make sure you have done each step correctly before you go on to the next step.*

Step 1:   Open a new sketch and draw a vertical segment (approximately 2 inches long) in your sketch.

   a. Go to the File menu and choose **New Sketch.**

   b. Click on the **Segment** tool .

   c. Click and drag to draw a vertical segment in your sketch. (Select point **A** first and drag upward to point **B.**

Step 2:   Mark point **A** as center.

   a. Click on the **Selection Arrow** tool and click in any blank space to deselect objects.

   b. Select point **A**, go to the Transform menu, and choose **Mark Center.**

Step 3:   Dilate point **B** upward by a scale factor of 3 to 2.

   a. Select point **B**. Go to the Transform menu and choose **Dilate.**

   b. In the Dilate dialog box, enter 3 in the top (numerator) box and 2 in the bottom (denominator) box. Click Dilate.

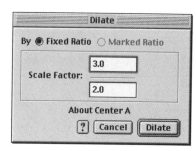

Dilate Dialog Box (Macintosh)

Step 4:   Mark point **B** as a center. Rotate point **B′** 45°. Then rotate point **B′** −45°.

   a. Click in any blank space to deselect objects.

   b. Select point **B**. Go to the Transform menu and choose **Mark Center.**

   c. Select point **B′** (the image of **B**). Go to the Transform menu and choose **Rotate.** In the Rotate dialog box, enter 45° and click Rotate.

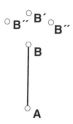

d. Click in any blank space to deselect objects.

e. Repeat step c, except this time enter −45° as the angle of rotation.

Now you will set up the recursive steps to create new stages for your fractal.

Step 5: Iterate on points **A** and **B**.

a. Click in any blank space to deselect objects.

b. Select point **A** and then point **B**. Go to the Transform menu and choose **Iterate.**

You may have to drag the Iterate dialog box to a new location so that you can see all the points in your sketch.

c. Click on point **B** to set it as the image of point **A**.

d. Click on the **B´´** (on the left) to set it as the image of **B**.

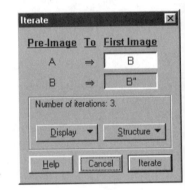

Iterate Dialog Box (Windows)

Step 6: Add a new mapping using points **B** and **B´´** (on the right).

a. Click on Structure and choose **Add New Map.**

b. Click on point **B** to set it as the image of point **A**.

c. Click on **B´´** (on the right) to set it as the image of **B**.

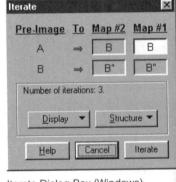

Iterate Dialog Box (Windows)

Step 7: Set your iterations to show only non-point images.

a. Click on Structure and choose **Only Non-Point Images.** Except for the original points you constructed, you should see only segments in your fractal.

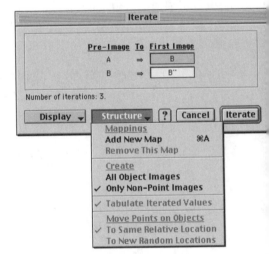

Structure Panel (Macintosh)

Step 8: Increase the stages of your fractal.

a. Click on Display and choose **Increase Iterations +.** You should now see more stages of your binary tree fractal.

b. You may repeat step a to see more stages of your binary tree fractal.

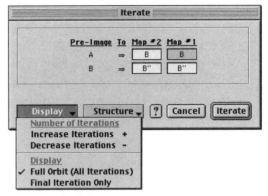

Display Panel (Macintosh)

Step 9: View the final version of your fractal.

a. Click Iterate.

b. You may hide all points if you wish. Your binary tree should look similar to the one below.

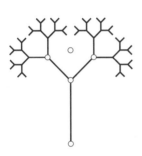

Constructing a Sierpiński Gasket Fractal

You will use Sketchpad to create the first stages of a Sierpiński gasket fractal. Follow the directions below. Whenever needed, use the detailed instructions marked by . In this construction, it is important to follow the selection order exactly as it is described. *Make sure you have done each step correctly before you go on to the next step.*

Step 1:   Construct a triangle **ABC** and its triangle interior.

a. Go to the File menu and choose **New Sketch.**

b. Use the **Segment** tool ▱ to construct a triangle.

c. Use the **Text** tool $\boxed{A}$ to label the points to match the diagram. (Remember that you can double-click on a label with the **Text** tool $\boxed{A}$ to change the label name.)

d. Click on the **Selection Arrow** tool $\boxed{\nwarrow}$ and click in any blank space to deselect objects.

e. Select the vertices of the triangle **ABC** *in that order*. Go to the Construct menu and choose **Triangle Interior.**

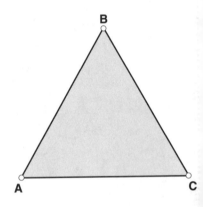

Step 2:   Construct the midpoints of the sides of △**ABC**.

a. Click in any blank space to deselect objects.

b. Click on the three sides of your triangle to select them.

c. Go to the Construct menu and choose **Midpoints.**

d. Relabel the points, if necessary, to match the diagram.

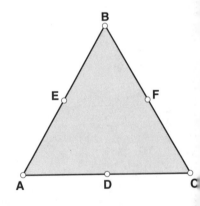

Step 3:   Iterate on the points **A**, **B**, and **C**.

a. Using the **Selection Arrow** tool $\boxed{\nwarrow}$, click in any blank space to deselect objects.

Geometry Activities for Middle School Students with The Geometer's Sketchpad
©2004 by Key Curriculum Press

b. Select points **A**, **B**, and **C** (in that order), go to the Transform menu and choose **Iterate.**

You may have to drag the Iterate dialog box to a new location so that you can see all the points in your sketch.

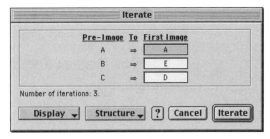

Iterate Dialog Box (Macintosh)

c. Click on point **A** to set it as the image of point **A**.

d. Click on point **E** to set it as the image of point **B**.

e. Click on point **D** to set it as the image of point **C**.

Step 4: Add a new mapping using points **E**, **B**, and **F**.

a. Click on Structure and choose **Add New Map.**

b. Click on point **E** to set it as the image of point **A**.

c. Click on point **B** to set it as the image of point **B**.

d. Click on point **F** to set it as the image of point **C**.

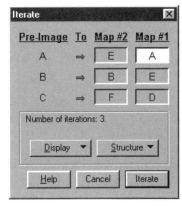

Iterate Dialog Box (Windows)

Step 5: Add a new mapping using points **D**, **F**, and **C**.

a. Click on Structure and choose **Add New Map.**

b. Click on point **D** to set it as the image of point **A**.

c. Click on point **F** to set it as the image of point **B**.

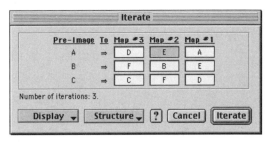

Iterate Dialog Box (Macintosh)

d. Click on point **C** to set it as the image of point **C**.

Step 6: Set your iterations to show only non-point images.

a. Click on Structure and choose **Non-Point Images Only.** You should see only segments in your fractal except for the original points you constructed.

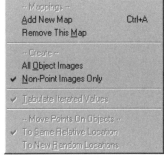

Structure Panel (Windows)

Step 7: Set your iterations to show the final iteration only and then iterate.

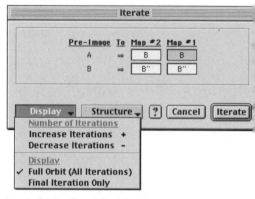

Iterate Dialog Box (Macintosh)

a. Click on Display and choose **Final Iteration Only.**

b. Click Iterate. You should see a figure similar to the one below.

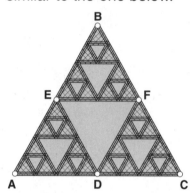

Step 8: Show the most recent iterated images and increase and decrease the stages of your fractal.

a. Click in any blank space to deselect objects.

b. Click on the center of the original interior of the triangle to select it.

c. Go to the Display menu and choose **Hide Triangle.** This should reveal the iterated image.

d. Drag a marquee around the entire figure and use the Plus (+) and Minus (–) keys to experiment with different numbers of iterations.

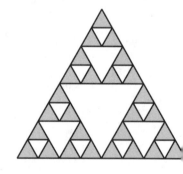

e. Click in any blank space to deselect objects. Click on the **Point** tool ⊡, go to the Edit menu and choose **Select All Points.** Go to the Display menu and choose **Hide Points.**

Your Sierpiński gasket should look similar to the one shown here.

Constructing a Dragon Fractal

You will use Sketchpad to create the first stages of a dragon fractal. Follow the directions below. Whenever needed, use the detailed instructions marked by . In this construction, it is important to follow the selection order exactly as described. *Make sure you have done each step correctly before you go on to the next step.*

Step 1: Construct a horizontal segment $\overline{AB}$ in your sketch.

    a. Go to the File menu and choose **New Sketch.**

    b. Use the **Segment** tool ☑ to construct a horizontal segment about 2 inches long in the sketch.

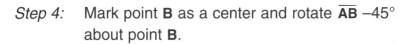

    c. Use the **Text** tool Ⓐ to label the points to match the diagram. (Remember that you can double-click on a label with the **Text** tool Ⓐ to change the label name.)

Step 2: Mark point **A** as a center.

    a. Click on the **Selection Arrow** tool Ⓚ and click in any blank space to deselect objects.

    b. Select point **A**. Go to the Transform menu and choose **Mark Center.**

Step 3: Rotate $\overline{AB}$ 45° about point **A**.

    a. Select $\overline{AB}$.

    b. Go to the Transform menu and choose **Rotate.**

    c. In the Rotate dialog box, choose **By Fixed Angle** and enter 45 in the Angle box. Click Rotate.

Rotate Dialog Box (Windows)

Step 4: Mark point **B** as a center and rotate $\overline{AB}$ −45° about point **B**.

    a. Click in any blank space to deselect objects.

    b. Select point **B**. Go to the Transform menu and choose **Mark Center.**

    c. Select $\overline{AB}$.

    d. Go to the Transform menu and choose **Rotate.**

Rotate Dialog Box (Macintosh)

e. In the Rotate dialog box, choose **By Fixed Angle** and enter −45. Click Rotate.

Step 5: Construct the intersection point of the rotated segments.

a. Select the two new segments (click on one or both of the two new segments until both are selected).

b. Go to the Construct menu and choose **Intersection.**

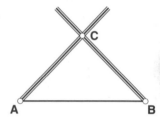

Step 6: Hide the two rotated segments.

a. Click in any blank space to deselect objects. Click on both the new segments to select them.

b. Go to the Display menu and choose **Hide Segments.**

Step 7: Construct $\overline{AC}$ and $\overline{BC}$ and hide $\overline{AB}$.

a. Select point **A** and then point **C**.

b. Go to the Construct menu and choose **Segment.** Click in any blank space to deselect objects.

c. Select point **B** and then point **C**.

d. Go to the Construct menu and choose **Segment.**

e. Using the **Selection Arrow** tool ⬉, click in any blank space to deselect objects.

f. Click on $\overline{AB}$ (not its endpoints). Go to the Display menu and choose **Hide Segment.**

Step 8: Iterate on points **A** and **B**.

a. Using the **Selection Arrow** tool ⬉, click in any blank space to deselect objects.

b. Select points **A** and **B** (in that order) and then go to the Transform menu. Choose **Iterate.**

You may have to drag the Iterate dialog box to a new location so you can see all the points in your sketch.

Iterate Dialog Box (Windows)

c. Click on point **A** to set it as the image of point **A**.

d. Click on point **C** to set it as the image of point **B**.

Step 9: Add a new mapping to points **B** and **C**.

a. Click on Structure and choose **Add New Map.**

b. Click on point **B** to set it as the image of point **A**.

c. Click on point **C** to set it as the image of point **B**.

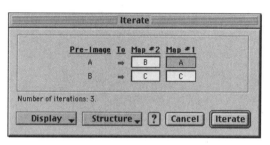

Iterate Dialog Box (Macintosh)

Step 10: Set your iterations to show only non-point images.

a. Click on Structure and choose **Only Non-Point Images.** You should see only segments in your fractal except for the original points you constructed.

Step 11: Set your iterations to show the final iteration only and then iterate.

a. Click Display and choose **Final Iteration Only.**

b. Click Iterate. You should see a figure similar to the one at right.

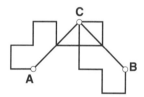

Step 12: Show the final iterated images and increase and decrease the stages of your fractal.

a. Click in any blank space to deselect objects. Click on $\overline{AC}$ and $\overline{BC}$.

b. Go to the Display menu and choose **Hide Segments.** This should reveal the iterated image.

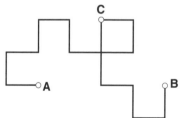

c. Drag a marquee around the entire figure and use the Plus (+) and Minus (−) keys to experiment with different numbers of iterations.

d. Click in any blank space to deselect objects. Click on the **Point** tool ⌷, go to the Edit menu, and choose **Select All Points.** Go to the Display menu and choose **Hide Points.**

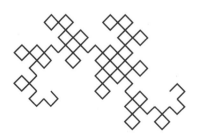

Shortcuts with The Geometer's Sketchpad

There are two types of shortcuts you can perform with Sketchpad. The first type uses the Command key (⌘) on Macintosh keyboards or the Control key (Ctrl) on Windows keyboards and another keystroke. Each shortcut is listed with the appropriate menu item.

Keystroke	Result	Keystroke	Result
⌘Z or Ctrl+Z	Undo	⌘H or Ctrl+H	Hide objects
⌘R or Ctrl+R	Redo	⌘K or Ctrl+K	Show or hide labels
⌘A or Ctrl+A	Select all	⌘T or Ctrl+T	Trace objects
⌘N or Ctrl+N	Open a new sketch	⌘I or Ctrl+I	Construct point at intersection
⌘O or Ctrl+O	Open dialog box for files	⌘M or Ctrl+M	Construct point at midpoint
⌘W or Ctrl+W	Close file	⌘L or Ctrl+L	Construct segment, ray, or line
⌘P or Ctrl+P	Construct interior of polygon, circle, or arc sector	Shift+⌘F or Shift+Ctrl+F	Mark a center
⌘S or Ctrl+S	Save file	⌘Q or Ctrl+Q	Quit or exit Sketchpad

The second type of shortcut uses the Sketchpad tools. When performed correctly, such shortcuts result in constructions that are just as sound as those made by using the commands from the menu.

Objective	Technique
Mark a mirror.	Using the **Selection Arrow** tool [↖], double-click on the segment, ray, or line you wish to be the mirror.
Mark a center.	Using the **Selection Arrow** tool [↖], double-click on the point you wish to be the center.
Construct a segment, ray, or line through two given points.	Using the **Segment** [╱], **Ray** [↗], or **Line** tool [↗], click on the first point and then click on the second point.
Construct a circle using two given points, one as the center and the other as a point on the circle.	Using the **Compass** tool [⊙], click on the point you wish to be the center and then click on the second point.
Construct the intersection point(s) of two given objects.	Using the **Selection Arrow** tool [↖], or using the **Point** tool [•], click on the point of intersection. (This method is not as foolproof for beginners.) *Note:* You can also draw segments, rays, lines, and circles to intersections without first constructing the point at the intersection.